NOVELLO EASY CHORALS

20 very easy flexible arrangements for choir
with piano accompaniment and digital practice tools

NOVELLO

Published by
Novello Publishing Limited

Exclusive Distributors:
Hal Leonard
7777 West Bluemound Road
Milwaukee, WI 53213
Email: info@halleonard.com

Hal Leonard Europe Limited
42 Wigmore Street
Marylebone, London, W1U 2RY
Email: info@halleonardeurope.com

Hal Leonard Australia Pty. Ltd.
4 Lentara Court
Cheltenham, Victoria, 3192 Australia
Email: info@halleonard.com.au

Order No. NOV167310
ISBN 978-1-78760-044-7

Edited by Jonathan Wikeley.
Music engraved and processed by Sarah Lofthouse, SEL Music Art Ltd.
Audio mixed and mastered by Jonas Persson.
Piano recorded by Martyn Noble.
Digital content managed by James Welland.
Design and layout by Ruth Keating.

Printed in the EU.

www.halleonard.com

CONTENTS

PREFACE

Three things. Choir. Singer. Conductor. The conductor makes all the decisions. The singer does what they say, and if the whole choir does it correctly, it comes out right. Right?

Maybe not. *Novello Easy Chorals* aims to help you the singer, your choir, and your conductor to work together as one unit. It aims to be flexible not only through the arrangements, which can be sung in many different ways and with different numbers of voice parts, but to encourage responsibility as a singer, and flexibility in how you think of your choir, your fellow singers and your conductor.

Each piece in the book comes with an introduction which offers warm-ups, vocal exercises and performance tips relating to the piece. Some are for the individual, some are for the choir as a whole. Some offer technical advice on how to improve your singing - such as how to breathe well; how to make a relaxed, resonant sound; how to come in together as a choir - while other ideas are performance based: how to make an impact on your audience, and suggestions on how you can enhance your performance through use of instruments or stage positioning. They aim to act as the start of an ideas bank to help you improve both as an individual singer and as a choir.

These introductions are for everyone - they are manifestly not just for the conductor! One of the things that makes singing in a choir so enjoyable is that feeling of being completely in sync with your fellow musicians - those moments when it all clicks, and you're neither following nor leading, but all making music together. To do that, we all need to take responsibility - singer, conductor, and choir as a whole.

Sure, a certain amount of technical help is useful - and this book offers that - but a confidence and trust in your ability and that of the singers around you will reap huge rewards. You may only have been singing in a choir for a week and have no idea how to read music, but if you look up, listen to your fellow singers and work together, you can achieve amazing results in no time at all.

Finally, *Novello Easy Chorals* is designed to give your choir fun, accessible repertoire, which you can shape to the strengths and needs of your choir, and which will blow away your audience. Happy singing!

HOW TO USE THE BOOK AND INTERACTIVE RESOURCES

The arrangements are flexible in nature – there is no one way of singing each piece. Every piece can be sung in unison, and all the other parts can be added as required. The pieces can be sung at treble pitch as indicated, but can also be sung an octave lower for men's voices, or a combination of both. Do explore different combinations of voice parts. The 'Performance ideas' section of the introductions gives specific performance suggestions for each piece.

The online interactive resources mean you can practise or sing along to the accompaniments anytime and anywhere.

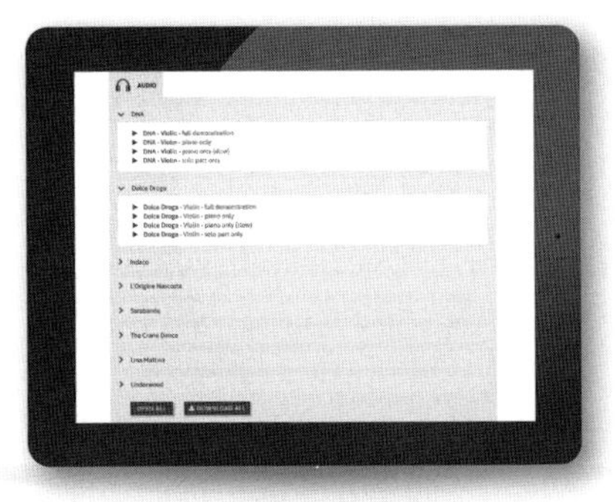

Practice tracks make it easy for you to rehearse your part while hearing the accompaniment and other voices.

The included piano recordings enable you to accompany the choir in any space or venue.

SoundCheck

powered by **Match My Sound**

What is it?

Your music book is supported by cutting-edge, interactive technology that gives you instant feedback on your practice. Each piece in the book is available online as an interactive exercise to enhance your learning, giving you instant feedback on aspects of your singing such as tuning and rhythm.

Start off in Practice mode and use the intuitive tools to enhance your learning experience.

SoundCheck is an interactive practice app that enables you to practise music your way.

Did you know?

- You can use the looping tool to go over tricky passages multiple times.
- You can adjust the speed of the piece or exercise by using the tempo tool.

When you're ready, switch to Perform mode to beat the exercises and receive instant feedback on your performance.

You will receive a star rating out of five and a percentage score for:

- Progress (how much of the piece you played).
- Performance (how well you played it).

All the stars you've earned in your book are saved, showing your overall progress – keep practising to collect them all!

Feedback from your performance is shown underneath the music.

The feedback screen scores your performance and gives you tips on how to improve.

SINGING TIPS AND WARM-UPS

Each piece comes with a number of singing tips and warm-ups that look at a different aspect of performance. Many of these are applicable to other pieces; the list below shows where you can find exercises on different subjects, so you can use them whenever you want to focus on a particular idea.

Idea	Page
Pulse and rhythm	1(i), 54(ii), 64(i), 71(i), 79(i), 85(i & ii), 91(ii)
Listening and thinking ahead	1(ii), 79(i), 91(i)
Relaxed singing	4(i), 8(i), 23(all), 28(ii), 54(i), 99(i), 104(i & ii), 109(i & ii), 114(i), 123(i)
Singing vowels	4(i), 23(all), 54(i), 104(ii), 114(i)
Encouraging independence	4(ii), 11(ii), 18(ii), 35(i), 71(ii)
Tuning	8(i), 23(iii), 35(i), 91(i), 99(ii)
Dynamics	8(ii), 28(ii), 64(ii), 123(i & ii)
Performing ideas	11(i), 49(ii), 79(ii), 114(ii)
Singing as a unit	18(i), 49(i), 71(ii), 79(i)
Breathing	23(ii), 28(i), 49(i), 99(i & ii), 109(i)
Singing consonants	35(ii), 79(ii), 104(ii)
Physical warmups	109(i & ii)

GO DOWN, MOSES

The spiritual 'Go Down, Moses' tells the Old Testament story of Moses demanding the release of the Israelites from slavery in Egypt. Despite the serious nature of the text ('if not, I'll strike your first-borns dead'), this arrangement is intended to give your choir the opportunity to get its teeth into a lighter style of gospel music.

1 A really solid pulse is important here, as the melody bounces off it. Tread the pulse (in this case, four crotchet beats per bar) – or walk around the room to it and, when it is stable, clap or say the rhythm of the words over the top.

Once you have managed this, try it again, but this time tread a pulse of two minim beats per bar, i.e. the pulse becomes twice as slow, but the rhythm of the words stays the same speed.

2 Call and response is an integral part of this piece, and plays an important part in gospel music generally. Choose a leader from your choir (or several people in turn) to make up a one-bar rhythm which the rest of your choir then copies. Try to keep the calls and responses continuous – so the response follows on directly from the call, and the next call follows on directly from the previous response. This is a great way to encourage listening and thinking ahead – a vital part of singing in a choir.

If this feels a bit safe and stable, you can make the exercise considerably more entertaining by asking your leaders to make up both a rhythm and words to go with it on the spot (still in one-bar phrases as above). You might want to pick a subject to improvise around – this can be anything from how to make the best breakfast, to the reasons your choir is the greatest, or anything in between. Either way, general mirth is usually the result. How many bars can you continue before it breaks down?

In the chorus, the melody is in Voice 1. To sing the piece with one part only, singers should sing all the words in the verses, i.e. both 'When Israel was in Egpyt's land / Let my people go'. The call-and-response patterns throughout can be allocated however you like – the opening and closing verses could be sung with two equal groups, and the middle verse sung with a soloist doing the 'calling' (Voice 1) and the whole chorus 'answering' (Voice 2), for example.

Finger clicking, clapping, stepping from side to side, and even vocal improvisation should give you plenty of opportunity to make this simple arrangement fun and rewarding for your choir.

GO DOWN, MOSES

Traditional
arr. Thomas Lydon

Sassy

VOICE 1

mf

1. When Is - rael was in
(2.) spake the Lord, bold
(3.) they had reached the

VOICE 2

Sassy

PIANO

mf

4

V.1

E - gypt's land,
Mo - ses said:
oth - er shore,

Op -
If
They

V.2

mf

Let my peo - ple go.

7

V.1

- pressed so hard they could not stand.
not, I'll smite your first-borns dead.
let the song of tri - umph soar.

V.2

Let my peo-ple go.

11
V.1
f
Go down, Mo-ses, way down in E-gypt's land,
V.2
f
Go down, Mo-ses, way down in E-gypt's land,
f
15
p
Tell old Pha-raoh to let my peo-ple go.
1, 2.
p
Tell old Pha-raoh to let my peo-ple go.
p
sub. p
19
2. Thus
3. When
3.
mf
f
Let my peo-ple go!
mf
f
Let my peo-ple go!
sub. p
f

AMAZING GRACE

'Amazing Grace' is a popular hymn, published in 1779, with words by the poet, clergyman and reformed slave trader John Newton, who turned to Christianity after his ship was miraculously saved at sea.

1 Sing the exercise below, thinking about keeping your voice in the same place as you do so by using the techniques described in exercise 1 on page 114. Start by singing it to *ah*, with your mouth wide open and relaxed (you should be able to fit at least two fingers between your teeth as you do so). Take a good, relaxed breath before you sing, and imagine looking down on to the phrase from above it - so that you can 'drop down' onto the last note, rather than stretch up to it.

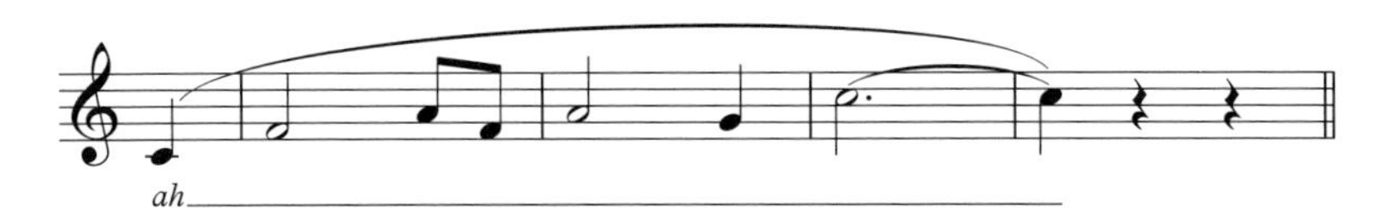

Now try the same exercise to *eh*, *ee*, *or*, and *oo*. When you reach the more closed vowels, such as *ee* and *oo*, try to keep your mouth open in the same way as when you sang the *ah* vowel (think vertically, as though you mouth is making the shape of an egg balancing on its end), as this keeps your mouth and throat open and relaxed.

Test the difference between singing the exercise to *ah* with an open and a less open mouth. Also try singing it to *ee*, with your mouth open wide horizontally, and then open vertically as described above. Can you hear the difference in the sound? The latter is much more resonant and projects much more.

2 The melody to 'Amazing Grace' is one of the most well known in the world (though there are variants - so make sure you are singing what is printed!). The piano accompaniment sometimes uses some slightly more unusual chords, but the melody needs to continue confidently no matter what happens in the piano part. Practise this by singing the tune and asking your accompanist (or the online accompaniment) to stop playing whenever they like before dropping the accompaniment back in again. Aim to keep the tune going regardless of whatever is happening underneath.

The piece can be sung in unison or in two parts. The melody is in Voice 1 for all verses except the last, when it switches to Voice 2.

AMAZING GRACE

Traditional
arr. Phoebe McFarlane

21
VOICE 1
V.1
man - y dan - gers, toils and snares, I have al -
(4.) Lord has pro - mised good to me, His word my
VOICE 2
V.2
man - y dan - gers, toils and snares, I have al -
(4.) Lord has pro - mised good to me, His word my
26
V.1
-read - y come; 'Tis grace hath brought me safe thus
hope se - cures; He will my shield and por - tion
V.2
-read - y come; 'Tis grace hath brought me safe thus
hope se - cures; He will my shield and por - tion
32
1.
2.
V.1
far, And grace will lead me home. 4. The
be, As long as life en - - dures.
V.2
far, And grace will lead me home. 4. The
be, As long as life en - - dures.

38
V.1
V.2
f
5. When we've been there ten thou - sand years, Bright
5. When we've been there ten thou - sand years, Bright
43
shin - ing as the sun, We've no less days to
shin - ing as the sun, We've no less days to
49
rit.
sing God's praise Than when we'd first be - gun.
sing God's praise Than when we'd first be - gun.

STEAL AWAY

'Steal Away' is an African-American spiritual from the 19th Century. It has been arranged by many composers and singers over the years, including by Michael Tippett as one of five spirituals from his oratorio *A Child Of Our Time*. The melody is deeply expressive and soulful. The simple tune and words mean that all your attention can be given to making as beautiful a sound as possible.

1 'Steal Away' is a work of elegance and dignity, and as such, it's important to get the details right. Divide your choir into three parts and build up the chord below. The notes can be sung at any octave and in any part. Start with the first note - the root of the chord. Then add the second - the fifth of the chord. As much as possible, try to avoid using the piano to help you. Once you have a beautiful, ringing fifth, add the third of the chord to create a major triad. Breathe gently whenever you need to, and keep the sound going. Listen to the other singers and aim for a perfectly in-tune sound.

2 Now you have your chord, you can experiment with it (you can do the same with a single note on your own). This exercise is good for exploring dynamics. While you sing the chord, hold an imaginary ball on either side in front of your stomach. Let the ball grow in size as you increase the volume (a crescendo), pushing your hands further apart, and then reduce it as you decrease the volume (a diminuendo). Try to make the change in volume as smooth and beautifully graded as possible - this is easier to do when you get louder than it is when you get quieter!

The melody is in Voice 1, and the piece can be sung in unison or in two parts. You can be flexible with the tempo - explore moving on slightly in the verses, and slowing back down for the chorus.

STEAL AWAY

Traditional
arr. Laurence Long

11
mf
V.1
1. My Lord, he calls me, he calls me by the
2. Green trees are bend - ing, poor sin - ners stand a -
mf
V.2
1. My Lord, he calls me, he calls me by the
2. Green trees are bend - ing, poor sin - ners stand a -
mf
14
V.1
thun - der;
-tremb - ling;
f
The trum-pet sounds with - in my soul, I
mf
V.2
thun - der;
-tremb - ling;
f
The trum-pet sounds with - in my soul, I
mf
f
mf
17
1.
2.
V.1
ain't got long to stay here.
stay here.
V.2
ain't got long to stay here.
stay here.

JOSHUA FIT THE BATTLE OF JERICHO

'Joshua Fit The Battle Of Jericho' is an African-American spiritual, thought to have been written by slaves in the early 19th Century. It tells the story of the Israelites at they attempt to conquer Canaan. The song is fast and exciting, and you can be as dramatic as you like in performance.

1 This piece works at different speeds and dynamics so long as the words are clearly enunciated. Explore singing the verses and choruses in different ways. Slow practice is helpful for getting the words and music together, but don't be afraid to take the tempo faster than that suggested by the metronome mark once you know it well. Try drawing the audience in with an excited, whispered tone, or emphasise the offbeats (the second and fourth beats) slightly for a more jazzy effect.

2 Sing the verse sections as a round to help develop independence of singing – it works in two or four parts, with each part starting a bar later than the previous part. If that is too easy, the canon will also work with each part starting two beats after the previous part. Verse 1 (bar 29) is easier than verse 2, as the latter starts on an upbeat.

The melody is in Voice 1, and the piece can be sung in unison or in two parts.

JOSHUA FIT THE BATTLE OF JERICHO

Traditional
arr. Dominic Veall

14
V. &2
Gi - de - on, you may talk a - bout the men of Saul, But there's
17
V. &2
none like good old Josh - u - a at the bat-tle of Je - ri - cho.
21
VOICE 1
V.1
Josh - ua fit the bat - tle of Je - ri - cho, Je - ri - cho,
VOICE 2
V.2
Josh - ua fit the bat - tle of Je - ri - cho, Je - ri - cho,
24
V.1
Je - ri - cho, Josh - ua fit the bat - tle of Je - ri - cho, and the
V.2
Je - ri - cho, Josh - ua fit the bat - tle of Je - ri - cho, and the

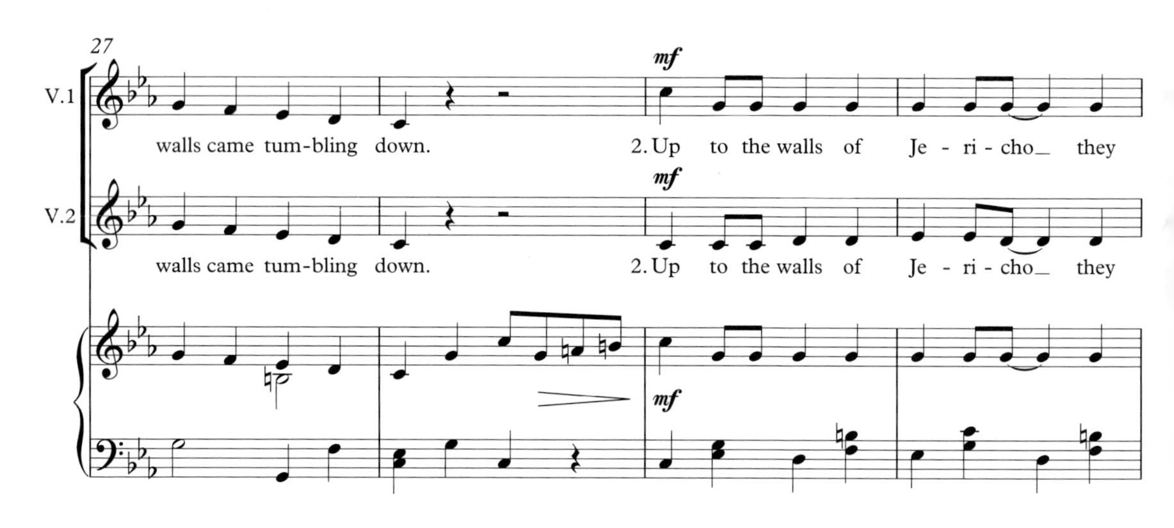
27
V.1
mf
walls came tum-bling down.
2. Up to the walls of Je - ri - cho_ they
V.2
mf
walls came tum-bling down.
2. Up to the walls of Je - ri - cho_ they
mf

31
V.1
f
marched with spear in hand,
'Go blow them ram horns',
V.2
f
marched with spear in hand,
'Go blow them ram horns',
f

34
V.1
Josh - ua cried,_ ''Cause the bat - tle is in my hand'.
V.2
Josh - ua cried,_ ''Cause the bat - tle is in my hand'.

37
V.1
V.2
mp
Josh - ua fit the bat - tle of Je - ri - cho, Je - ri - cho,
Josh - ua fit the bat - tle of Je - ri - cho, Je - ri - cho,
mp
40
Je - ri - cho, Josh - ua fit the bat - tle of Je - ri - cho, and the
Je - ri - cho, Josh - ua fit the bat - tle of Je - ri - cho, and the
43
ff
walls came tum - bling down. 3. Then the lamb, ram, sheep horns be -
walls came tum - bling down. 3. Then the lamb, ram, sheep horns be -
ff

46
V.1
-gan to blow and the trum-pets be - gan to sound, And Josh - ua com-mand-ed the
V.2
-gan to blow and the trum-pets be - gan to sound, And Josh - ua com-mand-ed the
50
V.1
child-ren to shout and the walls came tum - bling down.
V.2
child-ren to shout and the walls came tum - bling down.
53
V.1
f
Josh - ua fit the bat - tle of Je - ri - cho, Je - ri - cho,
V.2
f
Josh - ua fit the bat - tle of Je - ri - cho, Je - ri - cho,
f

56
V.1
Je - ri - cho, Josh-ua fit the bat-tle of Je - ri - cho, and the
V.2
Je - ri - cho, Josh-ua fit the bat-tle of Je - ri - cho, and the
59
cresc.
ff
walls came tum-bling down, and the walls came tum-bling down, and the
cresc.
ff
walls came tum-bling down, and the walls came tum-bling down, and the
cresc.
ff
63
walls came tum - bling down.
walls came tum - bling down.
sub. p

DOWN TO THE RIVER TO PRAY

The origins of 'Down To The River To Pray' are unknown – it has been described as a hymn, a spiritual or gospel song, and an Appalachian tune. The song has been covered by many artists, not least Alison Krauss, who sang it as part of the soundtrack to the film *O Brother, Where Art Thou?*

1 Although you can (and should) be flexible with how you divide up the parts in this piece, the vocal lines never change from verse to verse – only the accompaniment varies. When you are learning this piece, take the time to learn both (or even all three) parts. In addition to having something useful to do while other singers learn their notes, it will give you a much better sense of what is going on in the whole piece, and will help your choir sing as one unit. Learning each part together offers help in the form of strength in numbers. This is both a confidence booster, and speeds up the learning process.

2 Once you all have the tune firmly in your head, sing it as a canon – it doesn't really work as such, but it is a great exercise in maintaining independence while still listening to the other parts. You can try this in two or three parts. Make sure you move the parts around, so the same people don't always start!

The melody is in Voice 1, and the piece can be sung in unison, two or three parts. Both Voices 2 and 3 fit independently with the melody, and both can be used to create a two-part piece, or all three parts can be sung together.

Any of the accompaniments will fit with any combination of voice parts, and the vocal lines can all be sung without accompaniment. The accompaniments don't need to be played in order; you can repeat them or omit them as you wish. Be as free as you like when deciding how to sing each verse – the arrangement is not designed to be sung full in three parts all the way through!

This mesmerising tune can be performed in many ways and can be a real showstopper – think about how you can use your performance space to best effect. It can be used as an opener or a finisher to a concert – the choir can walk in (or out) singing the tune in unison, or each part can walk in as their part enters. You can start or finish with a solo voice, or accompany a solo with humming in the other voice parts.

You can add instruments to the mix, either playing the vocal lines or part of the accompaniment.

If the performance space allows, and you have enough singers, you can even spread around the whole audience, giving them a real surround-sound experience. The words are easy to learn, and the music never changes, so try memorising it and singing it off-copy. The piece is easy to keep together – try performing without your conductor, and really connect with your audience.

DOWN TO THE RIVER TO PRAY

Traditional
arr. Jonathan Wikeley

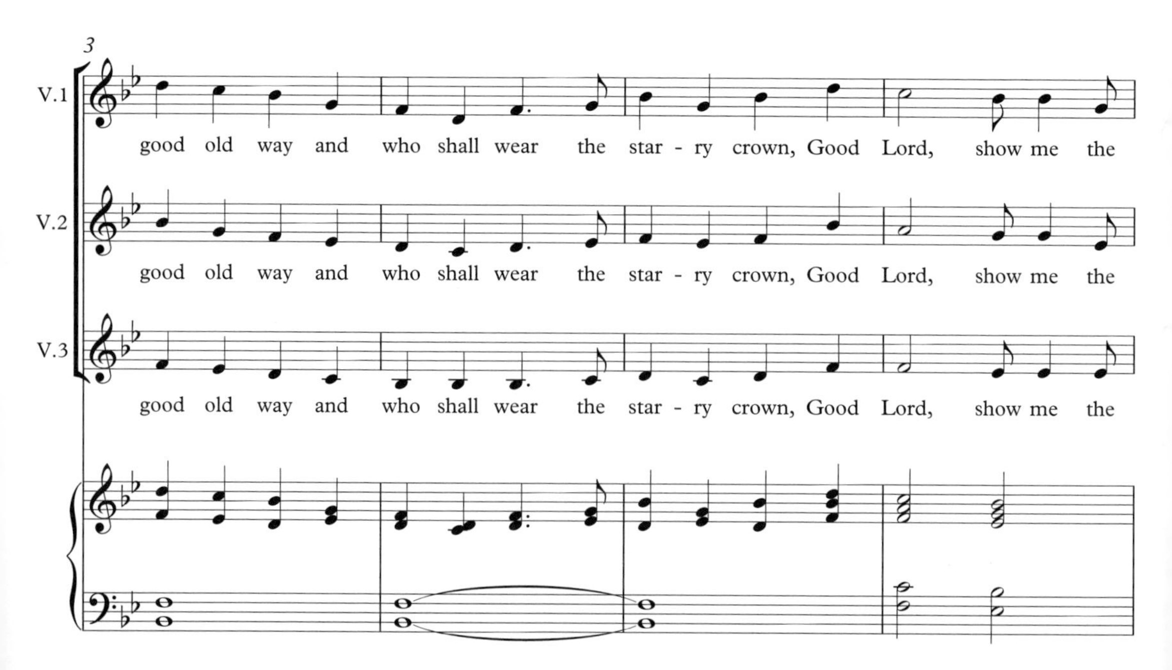

7
V.1
way. Oh sis - ters, broth - ers, fath - ers, moth - ers, sin - ners, child - ren, let's go down, let's go down, come on down,
V.2
way. Oh sis - ters, broth - ers, fath - ers, moth - ers, sin - ners, child - ren, let's go down, let's go down, come on down,
V.3
way. Oh sis - ters, broth - ers, fath - ers, moth - ers, sin - ners, child - ren, let's go down, let's go down, come on down,
12
V.1
Oh sis - ters, broth - ers, fath - ers, moth - ers, sin - ners, child - ren, let's go down, down to the riv - er to pray.
V.2
Oh sis - ters, broth - ers, fath - ers, moth - ers, sin - ners, child - ren, let's go down, down to the riv - er to pray.
V.3
Oh sis - ters, broth - ers, fath - ers, moth - ers, sin - ners, child - ren, let's go down, down to the riv - er to pray.

Accomp. 2
5
11
Accomp. 3
6
11
Accomp. 4
7

OVER THE RAINBOW

This ballad, originally from the film *The Wizard Of Oz,* has been sung by countless performers over the years, from Eva Cassidy to Placido Domingo, in dozens of musical styles.

1 The trick to making the big jump between the first two notes of each chorus (between 'some-' and 'where') is to keep a relaxed jaw and plenty of space in the back of the mouth – just like when you yawn.

Think about really opening up your mouth when you sing – try vocalising a big yawn. Apart from being satisfying to do, it opens up your mouth and throat, which will help you to create a relaxed, more resonant sound. Now sing the first two notes of the tune with your mouth as open as when you yawn. It will feel strange at first – it doesn't look as odd as it feels! Think about having an (imaginary) tennis ball in your mouth as you sing.

2 Remember that '-where' of 'somewhere' isn't the final destination of the first musical phrase – you need to head for the '-bow' of 'rainbow' (or even 'high', if you have the stamina). Sing the exercise below, making an open, resonant sound. Make sure you're standing nicely balanced, with relaxed arms, legs and shoulders. Take a relaxed breath in, and pace your breath so that you reach the final note of the exercise with breath to spare.

Once you've mastered that, try it again but more slowly. You can sing this to any vowel, but remember to keep your mouth and throat open as you sing.

3 The verse section of this song needs a bit a care. Sing the exercise below, nice and slowly; concentrate on making each note perfectly in tune. Think about opening up your mouth as you sing, maintain a beautiful smooth ribbon of sound, and aim to keep your voice (and your head!) in the same place (think down as you sing higher, and vice versa). Once you can do this, you can speed up the exercise, and sing it to different vowels.

The melody is in Voice 1, and the piece can be sung in unison or in two parts.

OVER THE RAINBOW

Words: E. Y. Harburg
Music: Harold Arlen, arr. Thomas Lydon

13
mf
Some - where o - ver the rain - bow skies are
mf
Some - where o - ver the rain - bow skies are
mf
16
dim.
blue, And the dreams that you dare to
dim.
blue, And the dreams that you dare to
dim.
19
mp
dream real - ly do come true. Some day I'll wish up - on a star and
mp
dream real - ly do come true. Some day I'll wish up -
mp

22
V.1
wake up where the clouds are far be - hind me, Where
V.2
- on a star be - hind me, Where
25
cresc.
trou-bles melt like lem-on drops, a - way a-bove the chim-ney tops, That's where you'll
cresc.
trou - bles melt like lem - on drops, That's where you'll
cresc.
28
f
find me. Some - where o - ver the rain - bow blue - birds
f
find me. Some - where o - ver the rain - bow blue - birds
f

32
dim.
fly, Birds fly o - ver the rain - bow, why then, oh why can't
dim.
fly, Birds fly o - ver the rain - bow, why then, oh why can't
dim.
36
p
I? If hap - py lit - tle blue-birds fly be - yond the rain- bow,
p
I? If hap - py lit - tle blue-birds fly be - yond the rain- bow,
p
39
Slower
f
pp
why, oh why, can't I?
f
pp
why, oh why, can't I?
Slower
f
pp

I DREAMED A DREAM

'I Dreamed A Dream' is from the musical *Les Misérables* by Claude-Michel Schönberg – the longest running musical in London's West End. The song is sung by the character Fantine, who has just lost her job and been thrown on to the streets.

Singing tips and warm-ups

1 Think about your breathing for each phrase in this piece – you need enough breath to carry you through the phrase, but you don't always have much time to take it. Start with a wide open mouth, breathe in as though you are horrified – a gasp. Feel the air instantly filling your body right down to the bottom of your abdomen. It doesn't matter if you make a noise – though do practise the same thing quietly, so you can't hear it in your performance!

This is an easy way to get a lot of air into your body very quickly. Put your hands on either side of your stomach as you breathe – you should be able to feel the air pushing your lower abdomen out as it rushes in.

2 Sing the exercise below. Take a deep, relaxed breath beforehand, ensuring you are standing well balanced on both feet. Try to make the crescendo and the diminuendo as even as possible – this is always easier when getting louder than softer, so think particularly carefully about the diminuendo. Always keep the tone relaxed – you never want to force the sound.

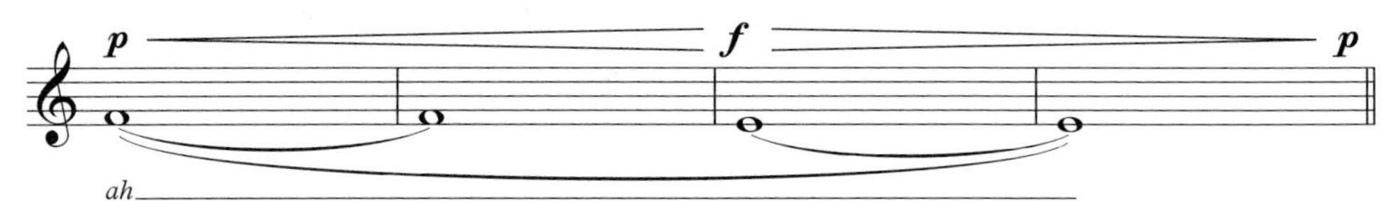

Now sing the next exercise in exactly the same way. This time, keep a flowing ribbon of sound as you change notes – think of the rising phrase as an escalator, rather than a series of steps. Try to keep the voice in the same place, using the techniques discussed in exercise 1 on page 114.

Performance ideas

The melody is in Voice 1, and the piece can be sung in unison or in two parts. The passage from bar 12–17 is rather low, and can be sung by Voice 2 alone if needed. The bracketed notes in the accompaniment at bar 46 are optional.

Feel free to be as over-the-top as you wish in your performance of this piece – it can withstand a good amount of drama in your singing. If it's too much, your conductor will tell you; but frankly, in a piece like this, that's unlikely to happen.

I DREAMED A DREAM

Words: Alain Boublil, Jean-Marc Natel & Herbert Kretzmer
Music: Claude-Michel Schönberg, arr. Jonathan Wikeley

8
V.1
I dreamed that love would nev - er die,
There was no ran - som to be paid,
V.2
I dreamed that love would nev - er die,
There was no ran - som to be paid,
10
V.1
I dreamed that God would be for - giv - ing.
No song un - sung, no wine un - tast - ed.
V.2
I dreamed that God would be for - giv - ing.
No song un - sung, no wine un - tast - ed.
12
V.1
mf
But the ti - gers come at night, with their voic - es soft as
V.2
mf
But the ti - gers come at night, with their voic - es soft as
mf

15
thun - der;
As they tear your hope a - part,
thun - der;
As they tear your hope a - part,
18
As they turn your dream to shame.
As they turn your dream to shame.
22
mp
He slept a sum - mer by my side,
He filled my days with end-less
mp
He slept a sum - mer by my side,
He filled my days with end-less
mp

25
V.1
won- der,
He took my child - hood in his stride,
V.2
won- der,
He took my child - hood in his stride,
28
V.1
But he was gone when au - tumn came.
V.2
But he was gone when au - tumn came.
31
V.1
f
And still I dreamed he'd come to me,
That we would live the years to -
V.2
f
And still I dreamed he'd come to me,
That we would live the years to -
f

34
-geth- er,
But there are dreams there can - not be,
-geth- er,
But there are dreams there can - not be,
37
And there are storms we can-not weath- er.
And there are storms we can-not weath- er.
I had a dream my life would
40
I had a dream my life would be,
So diff-'rent from this hell I'm
be
So diff-'rent from this hell I'm liv-ing,

43
V.1
liv - ing, So diff-'rent now from what it seemed,
V.2
So diff-'rent now from what it seemed,

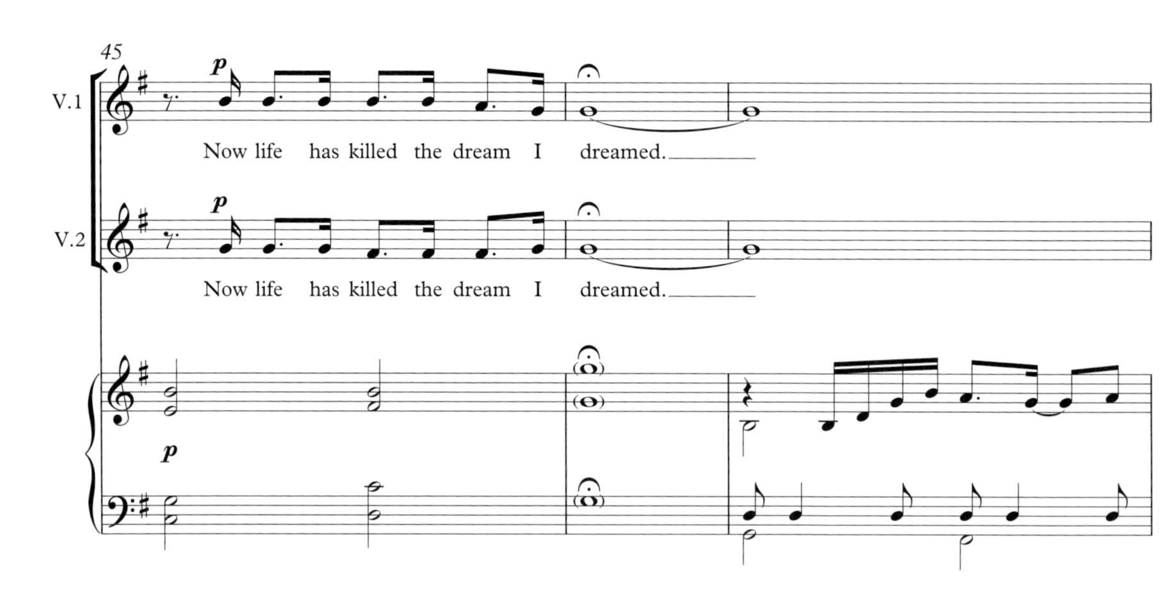
45
V.1
p
Now life has killed the dream I dreamed.
V.2
p
Now life has killed the dream I dreamed.
p

48
rit.
pp

THE RHYTHM OF LIFE

'The Rhythm Of Life' is a song set in an underground hippie network called the Rhythm of Life Church. The song is from the 1966 musical film *Sweet Charity* and was made famous by Sammy Davis Jr's performance as the church's 'daddy' in the 1969 film.

1 Apart from getting through a lot of words in a short space of time, this infectious piece requires an ability to sing independent lines while staying in time with everyone else. Sing the following exercise. Don't forget to think low as you sing up the scale, so your voice stays in the same place. Be careful when you reach '7' – it's the hardest note to tune!

Now sing the exercise again, but this time divide your choir into two parts; the second begins when the first part reaches the first asterisk. This exercises encourages independence – you need to think carefully about your own part – while at the same time creating an awareness of the other parts so everyone stays in time with each other.

Once you have mastered this, sing the same exercise in four parts. You can add endless variation to this classic exercise – try getting louder (or quieter) as you get higher, for example, or singing it at different speeds. The exercise also works upside down, starting on '8', and descending '8, 878, 87678' and so on.

2 The words are a huge part of any vocal piece, but are particularly important here. Practise whispering the words at the correct tempo, in rhythm, enunciating clearly so that you can hear every word. Now divide your choir into two parts and whisper alternate four-bar phrases to each other. Which side is the clearest?

The melody is in Voice 1, and the piece can be sung in unison, two or three parts. Don't be restricted by the labelling of the voice parts - feel free to share the parts around. There are no 'higher' or 'lower' parts in this piece, so you can split your choir up as freely as you like.

The rhythm needs to be absolutely solid throughout, but don't let this stop you tapping into the slightly unhinged, obsessive quality to the music. Really overdo the consonants. Your conductor will tell you if it's too much, but it's amazing how over the top you can be without it becoming too much for the audience.

THE RHYTHM OF LIFE

Words: Dorothy Fields
Music: Cy Coleman, arr. Dominic Veall

16
V. 1&2
wid - er screen.' And the voice said, 'Dad - dy, there's a mil - lion pig - eons

19
V. 1&2
Read - y to be hooked on new re - li - gions. Hit the road, Dad - dy, leave your

22
V. 1&2
mf
com-mon-law wife; Spread the re - li - gion of The Rhy-thm of Life.' And the

25
V. 1&2
rhy-thm of life is a pow-er-ful beat, Puts a tin-gle in your fin-gers and a

28
V. 1&2
tin - gle in your feet, Rhy - thm in your bed - room,
30
V. 1&2
rhy - thm in the street, Yes, the rhy - thm of life is a
32 VOICE 1
V.1
pow - er - ful beat, And the rhy - thm of life is a pow - er - ful beat, Puts a
VOICE 2
V.2
mf
pow - er - ful beat, Dad - dy, go,
35
V.1
tin - gle in your fin - gers and a tin - gle in your feet, Rhy - thm in your bed - room,
V.2
Go, go, go, Tell them

38
V.1
rhy-thm in the street, Yes, the rhy-thm of life is a pow-er-ful beat.
V.2
ev - 'ry - thing you know.
41
VOICES 1 & 2
mf
V. 1&2
Dad-dy spread the gos - pel in Mil - wau - kee, Took this walk - ie - talk - ie to
mf
44
V. 1&2
Rock - y Ridge; Blew his way to Can - ton, then to Scran - ton,
47
V. 1&2
Till he land-ed un-der the Man-hat - tan Bridge. Dad-dy was the new sen-sa-tion,

50
V. 1&2
got him - self a con - gre - ga - tion, Built up quite an op - er - a - tion
52
down be - low; With the pie-eyed pip - er blow - ing, while the mus - ca - tel was flow - ing,
55
All the cats were go, go, go - ing down be - low.
57
VOICE 1
mf
V.1
Dad - dy was the new sen - sa - tion,
VOICE 2
mf
V.2
Dad - dy was the new sen - sa - tion, got him - self a con - gre - ga - tion,

59
V.1
Got him-self a con - gre - ga - tion, All the cats were
V.2
Built up quite an op - e - ra - tion down be - low; With the pie-eyed pip - er blow-ing,
62
go, go, go - ing down be - low.
while the mus-ca - tel was flow-ing, All the cats were go, go, go - ing down be - low.
VOICES 1 & 2
65
mp poco a poco cresc.
V. 1&2
Flip your wings and fly to Dad - dy, Flip your wings and fly to Dad - dy,
mp poco a poco cresc.
69
Flip your wings and fly to Dad - dy, Fly, fly fly to Dad - dy.

73
VOICE 1
mf sempre cresc.
V.1
Take a dive and swim to Dad - dy, Take a dive and
VOICE 2
mf sempre cresc.
V.2
Take a dive and swim to Dad - dy, Take a dive and
mf sempre cresc.
76
swim to Dad - dy, Take a dive and
swim to Dad - dy, Take a dive and
78
swim to Dad - dy, Swim, swim, swim to Dad - dy.
swim to Dad - dy, Swim, swim, swim to Dad - dy.
81
mp

VOICES 1 & 2
V. 1&2
To feel the rhy - thm of life, To feel the

V. 1&2
pow - er - ful beat, To feel the tin - gle in your fin - gers,

V. 1&2
To feel the tin - gle in your feet. And the rhy - thm of life is a

98
V. &2
pow - er - ful beat, Puts a tin - gle in your fin - gers and a tin - gle in your feet,
101
V. &2
Rhy - thm in your bed - room, rhy - thm in the street, Yes, the rhy - thm of life is a
104
VOICE 1
V.1
pow - er - ful beat. To feel the rhy - thm of life,
VOICE 2
V.2
pow - er - ful beat. And the rhy - thm of life is a pow - er - ful beat, Puts a
107
V.1
To feel the pow - er - ful beat,
V.2
tin - gle in your fin - gers and a tin - gle in your feet,

109
V.1
To feel the tin-gle in your fin-gers, to feel the
V.2
Rhy-thm in your bed-room rhy-thm in the street, Yes, the rhy-thm of life is a
112
VOICE 1
V.1
tin-gle in your feet. Dad - dy go,
VOICE 2
V.2
pow-er-ful beat. To feel the rhy-thm of life,
VOICE 3
V.3
pow-er-ful beat. And the rhy-thm of life is a pow-er-ful beat, Puts a
115
V.1
Go, go, go, Tell them
V.2
To feel the pow-er-ful beat, To feel the
V.3
tin-gle in your fin-gers and a tin-gle in your feet, Rhy-thm in your bed-room

118
V.1
ev - - 'ry - thing you know.
V.2
tin - gle in your fin - gers, To feel the tin - gle in your feet.
V.3
rhy - thm in the street, Yes, the rhy - thm of life is a pow - er - ful beat.

121
p poco a poco cresc.

125
VOICE 1 only
mp
V.1
Flip your wings to fly to your Dad - dy, Take a dive and
VOICES 1 & 2
mf
mp
mf

VOICES 1, 2 & 3
128
V. 1&2
swim to your Dad - dy,
Hit the floor and crawl to your Dad - dy,
131
V. 1,2, &3
Dad - dy we got the rhy - thm of life, of life, of life, of
134
VOICE 1
V.1
life, of life, of life.
Yeah!
Yeah!
VOICES 2 & 3
V. 2&3
life, of life, of life.
Yeah!
Yeah!
138
V.1
Yeah!
Yeah!
V. 2&3
Yeah!
Yeah!

SIT DOWN, YOU'RE ROCKIN' THE BOAT

In this song, originally from the musical *Guys And Dolls*, a gambler describes a dream in which he is saved from hell and filled with Christian fervour. The musical recalls the atmosphere of the the New York underworld during the great depression.

1 There's a big pause before you come in at the start of the verse and the chorus, and it's important that everyone comes in together. This is more easily done than you might think – it just requires a bit of awareness of what everyone else is doing.

With the rest of your choir, choose a note or chord and remember it. Now shut your eyes, feel the choir around you, breathe in together and come in. Have the confidence in yourself and your fellow singers – no-one needs to lead or to follow.

2 Add a bit of spice to your performance. The first section should be sung with drama and wonder each time – don't be afraid to really ham it up, for instance by putting extra emphasis on the words 'laughed', 'passin' out the whiskey' (always gets a laugh) and 'washed me overboard' (perhaps get someone to shout 'oh nooooo!').

A little bit of attitude goes a long way in the chorus, especially if you can drop the 't' in 'sit down', and give the ensuing 'siddown' some twang and sass. Think about what else you might do to add a bit of zip to your performance.

The melody is in Voice 1, and the piece can be sung in unison or in two parts. The second part is optional in the verse section – or you can sing it in some verses and not in others.

SIT DOWN, YOU'RE ROCKIN' THE BOAT

Words and music: Frank Loesser
arr. Thomas Lydon

7
there I stood and I hol - lered, 'some - one fade me,' But the
there I stood nice - ly pass - in' out the whis - key, But the
as I sank, and I hol - lered, 'some - one save me,' That's the
oo
9
pas - sen - gers, they knew right from wrong.
pas - sen - gers were bound to re - sist.
mo - ment I woke up, thank the Lord.
f
For the
For the
And I
oo
11
Fast swing
peo - ple all said, 'sit down, sit down, you're rock - in' the
peo - ple all said, 'be - ware, you're on a heav - en - ly
said to my - self, 'sit down, sit down you're rock - in' the

14
V.1
boat.' Peo - ple all said, 'sit down, sit down,
trip.' Peo - ple all said, 'be - ware, be - ware,
boat.' Said to my - self, 'sit down, sit down,
V.2
boat.' Peo - ple all said, 'sit down, sit down,
trip.' Peo - ple all said, 'be - ware, be - ware,
boat.' Said to my - self, 'sit down, sit down,
17
V.1
you're rock - in' the boat; And the
you'll scut - tle the ship; And the
you're rock - in' the boat; And the
V.2
you're rock - in' the boat; And the
you'll scut - tle the ship; And the
you're rock - in' the boat; And the
19
V.1
dev - il will drag you un - der by the sharp la - pel of your
dev - il will drag you un - der by the fan - cy tie 'round your
dev - il will drag you un - der with a soul so heav - y you'd
V.2
dev - il will drag you un - der by the sharp la - pel of your
dev - il will drag you un - der by the fan - cy tie 'round your
dev - il will drag you un - der with a soul so heav - y you'd

22
V.1
check - ered coat; Sit down, sit down, sit down,
wick - ed throat; Sit down, sit down, sit down,
nev - er float; Sit down, sit down, sit down,
V.2
check - ered coat; Sit down, sit down, sit down,
wick - ed throat; Sit down, sit down, sit down,
nev - er float; Sit down, sit down, sit down,
24
1, 2.
sit down, sit down, you're rock - in' the boat.'
sit down, sit down, you're rock - in' the boat.'
sit down, sit down, you're rock - in' the boat.'
sit down, sit down, you're rock - in' the boat.'
sit down, sit down, you're rock - in' the boat.'
sit down, sit down, you're rock - in' the boat.'
mf
27
3.
2. I
3. And
oo
mp
ff

DON'T CRY FOR ME ARGENTINA

This song comes from Andrew Lloyd Webber's musical *Evita*. In the musical, the song is sung by Eva Perón, the First Lady of Argentina from 1946 until her death in 1952. She was a great activist and campaigner for labour rights and women's suffrage. 'Don't Cry For Me Argentina' is sung by Perón's spirit, and tells the people of Argentina not to mourn her.

1 In bar 63, you are asked to hum the tune. It's possible to make quite an open humming sound – think about keeping your mouth open inside (or holding an imaginary tennis ball in it) even when your lips are closed, and only close your lips gently. The exercise below will help you to keep an open humming sound. When you sing the hummed passage in the song, you can silently make the *ah* sound before the hum to ensure a good, round sound.

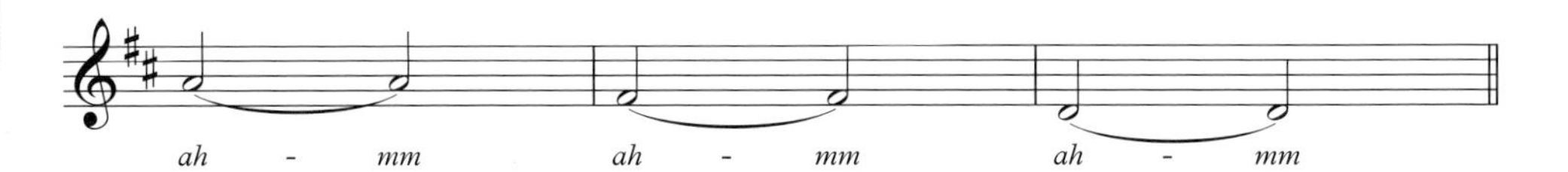

2 There are several passages of triplets in this piece. Think of them as lazy notes – they should really feel stretched out, which will help you land on the next beat exactly in time. Clap the exercise below. If you are doing it with your choir, clap both parts separately first. Then start one side clapping the crotchets (the pulse); once that is firmly together, add the triplet rhythm on top. On which beats of the bar do the two parts clap together?

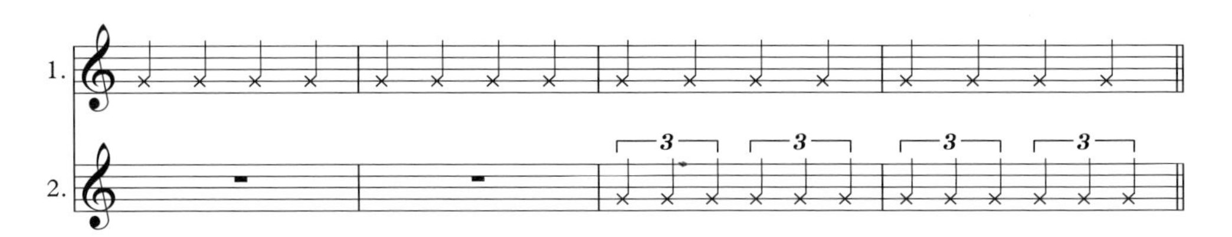

The melody is in Voice 1, and the piece can be sung in unison or in two parts.

DON'T CRY FOR ME ARGENTINA

Words: Tim Rice

Music: Andrew Lloyd Webber, arr. Phoebe McFarlane

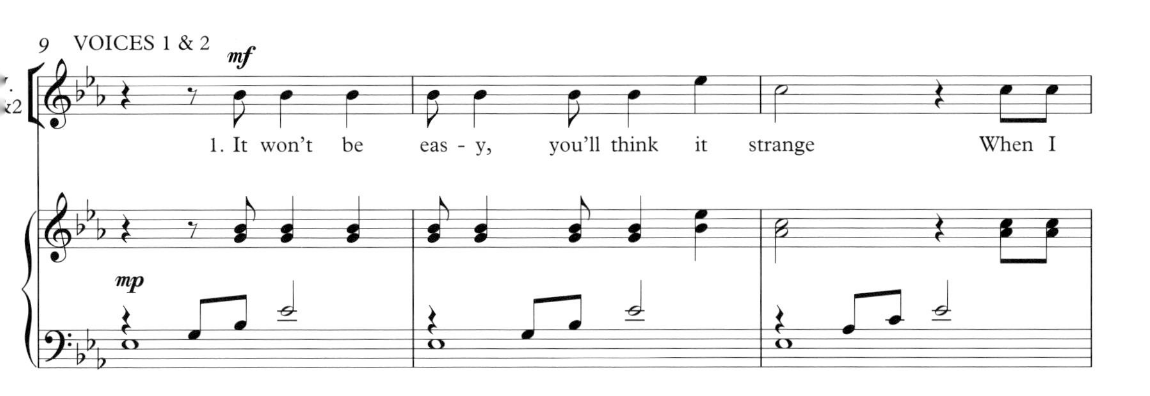

15
V. 1&2
all that I've done: You won't be - lieve me,
18
All you will see is a girl you once knew, Al - though she's dressed up to the
3
21
nines, At six - es and sev - ens with you.
24
V.1
mf
2. I had to let it hap - pen, I had to change; Could - n't
V.2
mp

27
stay all my life down at heel, Look-ing out of the win-dow, stay-ing
stay all my life down at heel, Look-ing out of the win-dow, stay-ing
30
out of the sun. So I chose free - dom,
out of the sun. So I chose free - dom,
33
Run-ning a - round try - ing ev - 'ry - thing new; But noth - ing im - pressed me at
Run-ning a - round try - ing ev - 'ry - thing new; But noth - ing im - pressed me at

36
V.1
all, I nev - er ex - pect - ed it to.
V.2
all, I nev - er ex - pect - ed it to.

Slow Tango feel
39
V.1
Don't cry for me, Ar - gen - ti - na,
The truth is I nev - er
V.2
Don't cry for me, Ar - gen - ti - na,
The truth is I nev - er
Slow Tango feel

42
V.1
left you, All through my wild days, my mad ex - ist - ence, I kept my
V.2
left you, All through my wild days, my mad ex - ist - ence, I kept my

45
prom - ise, don't keep your dis - tance._
prom - ise, don't keep your dis - tance._
48
mf
3. And as for for - tune, and as for fame: I
mf
3. And as for for - tune, and as for fame: I
mp
51
nev - er in - vit - ed them in, Though it seemed to the world they were
nev - er in - vit - ed them in, Though it seemed to the world they were

54
V.1
all I de - sired. They are il - lu - sions, They're
V.2
all I de - sired. They are il - lu - sions, They're

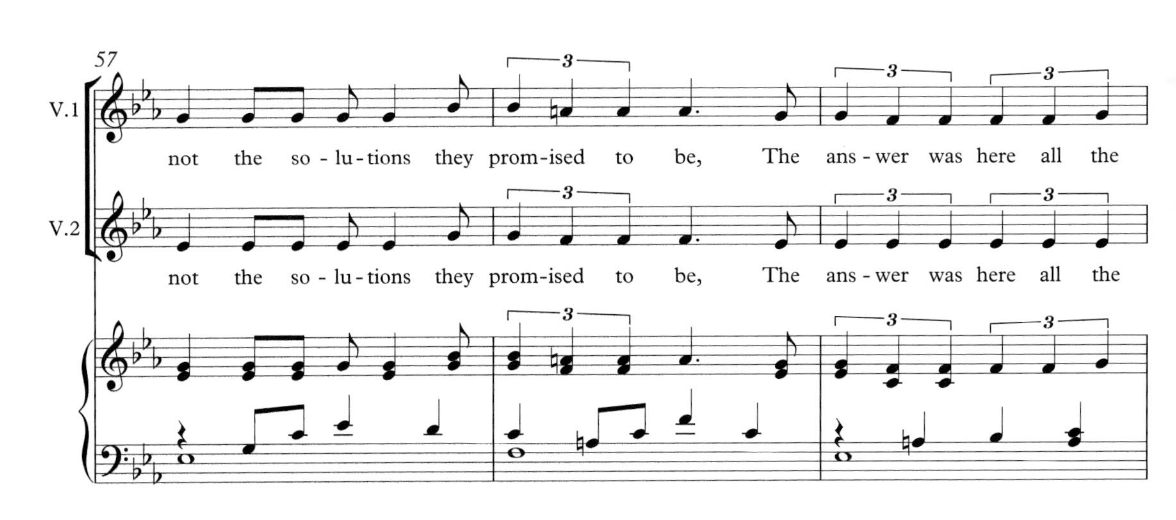
57
V.1
not the so - lu - tions they prom - ised to be, The ans - wer was here all the
V.2
not the so - lu - tions they prom - ised to be, The ans - wer was here all the

60
poco rall.
V.1
time: I love you and hope you love me.
V.2
time: I love you and hope you love me.
poco rall.

Slower
63
p
Don't cry for me, Ar - gen - ti - na,
mm
Slower
p colla voce
65
mm
68
mm

Tempo I
71
V.1
Don't cry for me, Ar - gen - ti - na
The truth is I nev - er
V.2
Don't cry for me, Ar - gen - ti - na,
The truth is I nev - er
Tempo I
74
left you, All through my wild days, my mad ex - ist - ence, I kept my
77
prom - ise, don't keep your dis - tance.

VOICES 1 & 2
79
mp
Have I said too much? There's noth - ing more I can think of to
p
81
say to you. But all you have to do is
84
rit.
a tempo
look at me to know that ev - 'ry word is true.
p
ff triumphant
molto
87
p

MAKE YOU FEEL MY LOVE

'Make You Feel My Love' was written by Bob Dylan and first released in 1997, sung by Billy Joel, before Dylan's own recording came out later in the same year. Since then it has been covered by many artists including Adele, on her debut album *19*.

1 Feeling the pulse - the regular beat that runs through a piece of music - is important in any song. In this song there are four crotchet beats in each bar. Either on your own or with your choir, tread the pulse with your feet. When you have a regular pulse going, clap the rhythm of the song while you keep the pulse going in your feet.

Once you can do this confidently, and when you know the tune well, try the same thing, but walking (carefully!) around. Having this sense of pulse when you sing a song helps to lock you into the rhythm and feel of the piece. You can either think the pulse in your head, or tap it gently with your big toe (so no-one else can hear it).

If you're feeling really confident, try treading only on the offbeats (beats 2 and 4) while you clap or sing the melody.

2 The dynamic at the beginning of the piece is *mezzo forte*. The phrase starts on a G - which is in the middle of most singers' registers - but it ends on a B, which is quite low for many singers. Generally speaking, lower notes tend to come across more quietly than higher notes. Try singing the phrases of this song, and think about where you might need to make your own dynamic adjustments to keep the overall dynamic the same. As well as singing this *mezzo forte*, try it *piano* and *forte* too (but be careful not to force the sound).

The melody is in Voice 1, and the piece can be sung in unison or in two parts. The *oohs* from bar 34–41 are optional and can be sung in one verse and not another, or not at all.

MAKE YOU FEEL MY LOVE

Words and music: Bob Dylan
arr. Phoebe McFarlane

13
V. 1&2
I could of - fer you a warm em - brace
I could hold you for a mil - lion years

15
1.
2.
V. 1&2
To make you feel my love.

VOICE 1
18
V.1
f
I know you have - n't made your mind up yet,
The storms are rag - ing on the roll - ing sea,
VOICE 2
V.2
f
I know you have - n't made your mind up yet,
The storms are rag - ing on the roll - ing sea,
mf

20
But I would nev - er do you wrong.
And on the high - way of re - gret.
Nev - er do you wrong.
High - way of re - gret.
22
I've known it from the mo - ment that we met;
The winds of change are blow - ing wild and free;
I've known it from the mo - ment that we met;
The winds of change are blow - ing wild and free;
24
No doubt in my mind where you be - long.
You ain't seen no - thin' like me yet.
No doubt in my mind where you be - long.
You ain't seen no - thin' like me yet.

26
V.1
mf
3. I'd go hun - gry, I'd go black and blue,
4. I could make you hap - py, make your dreams come true,
V.2
mf
3. I'd go hun - gry, I'd go black and blue,
4. I could make you hap - py, make your dreams come true,
mp
28
V.1
I'd go crawl - ing down the a - ve - nue.
Noth - ing that I would - n't do.
V.2
I'd go crawl - ing down the a - ve - nue.
Noth - ing that I would - n't do.
30
V.1
Know there's noth - ing that I would - n't do
Go to the ends of the earth for you
V.2
Know there's noth - ing that I would - n't do
Go to the ends of the earth for you

32
To Coda
V.1
To make you feel my love.
V.2
To make you feel my love.
34
ooh
ooh
f
36
ooh
ooh

38
V.1
ooh
V.2
ooh
40
D.S. al Coda
V.1
ooh
V.2
ooh
Coda
42
rit.
V.1
p
To make you feel my love.
V.2
p
To make you feel my love.
rit.
p

TEARS IN HEAVEN

Eric Clapton wrote 'Tears In Heaven' with Will Jennings in 1991 for the film *Rush*, but it is also a song in memory of his son Conor. The song is fairly slow and emotional, and is a good opportunity to practise sustaining longer notes and phrases.

1 Although the song itself is a fairly simple one, it can be tricky to remember exactly where each phrase begins. Tap or clap the pulse (the regular beat that runs through a piece of music - in this case four crotchet beats per bar) and say the lyrics over the top. Which phrases begin on the beat (i.e. at the same time as you clap) and which phrases begin off the beat (i.e. when you are not clapping)?

2 In this piece, the second voice part is sometimes below the tune, and sometimes above. One option, of course, would be to keep the lowest notes in the second voice part all the time, but if you can develop the confidence to stay strong on your line whether the voices around you are above or below you, you will ultimately become a much stronger choral singer. Once you know this piece well in two parts, try 'scrambling': each singers stands next to someone who is *not* singing their part.

This may feel chaotic at first, but once you get used to it, scrambling can be invaluable in helping a choir to sing together as one unit, as it makes hearing the other voice parts much easier - as well as being extremely satisfying to do.

The melody is in Voice 1, and the piece can be sung in unison or in two parts. Both parts are evenly pitched - there is no 'higher' or 'lower' part - indeed, Voice 2 sings both above and below the tune, so you can be free in your division of singers. In the first verse, the second part is optional.

TEARS IN HEAVEN

Words: Eric Clapton & Will Jennings
Music: Eric Clapton, arr. Dominic Veall

11
V.1
if I saw you in heav - en? I must be strong
if I saw you in heav - en? I'll find my way
V.2
if I saw you in heav - en? I must be strong
if I saw you in heav - en? I'll find my way
14
V.1
and car - ry on 'Cause I know
through night and day 'Cause I know
V.2
and car - ry on 'Cause I know
through night and day 'Cause I know
17
V.1
I won't be - long here in heav - en.
I just can't stay here in heav - en.
V.2
I won't be - long here in heav - en.
I just can't stay here in heav - en.

20
1.
2.

24
V.1
f
Time can bring you down, time can bend your knees,
V.2
f
Time can bring you down, time can bend your knees,
mf

27
V.1
Time can break you heart, have you beg - ging please,
V.2
Time can break you heart, have you beg - ging please,

30
V.1
beg-ging please.
V.2
beg-ging please.
f
33
36
40
mp
Be-yond the door
there's peace I'm sure
mp
Be-yond the door
there's peace I'm sure
p

43
V.1
And I know there'll be no more tears in heav - en.
V.2
And I know there'll be no more tears in heav - en.
47
V.1
Would you know my name
V.2
Would you know my name
51
V.1
if I saw you in heav - en? Would it be the same
V.2
if I saw you in heav - en? Would it be the same

55
V.1
if I saw you in heav - en?
I must be strong
V.2
if I saw you in heav - en?
I must be strong
59
V.1
and car - ry on
'Cause I know
I don't be - long
V.2
and car - ry on
'Cause I know
I don't be - long
63
rit.
V.1
here in heav - en.
V.2
here in heav - en.
rit.
pp

LULLABYE (GOODNIGHT, MY ANGEL)

Singing tips and warm-ups

'Lullabye (Goodnight, My Angel)' comes from Billy Joel's 1993 album *River Of Dreams*. The song had a long and varied development - at one point it was based on Gregorian chant with words in Latin. The final version was inspired by his seven-year-old daughter.

1 A relaxed sense of ebb and flow will play a large part in achieving a successful performance of this piece - it can be easy to make it sound like little more than a succession of quavers. Say the words quietly to yourself, either on your own or as a group. Each two-bar phrase wants to move forward slightly at the start, and pull back slightly at the end. Think of each phrase as being as flexible as a field of grass in the wind. Feel what your other singers are doing - there is no need to either lead or follow - just stay relaxed and have confidence in yourself and your fellow singers. By all means follow your conductor when you do this, but also practise singing the phrases without one.

Once you have got your two-bar phrases beautifully flexible, say or sing the last phrase of the verse (bar 17). Here, Joel extends the phrase, so it flows unexpectedly onwards for four bars, only holding up in the final bar. You can use exactly the same techniques as above to sing it, but difference can be magical.

2 While some of the pieces in this book require a sense of drama to hit the audience square between the eyes, this piece needs a slightly different approach. Rather than reaching out to your audience as you sing this, draw them in to you. A sense of poise and flexibility will help, but so will keeping a quiet dynamic - make the audience lean it to you.

Of course, you still need to hear the words. Divide your choir into two, and sing a verse of the song to each other. What is the quietest you can sing the verse but still be heard? Experiment with balancing dynamic range with clear consonants. Don't forget, while you need to understand the lyrics, this is a lullaby(e), so it's probably not the place for crazy-over-the-top consonants, such as you might get away with in 'The Rhythm of Life' or a similar piece.

Performance ideas

The melody is in Voice 1, and the piece can be sung in unison, two or three parts. The *doos* from bar 25–28 are optional. Both Voices 2 and 3 fit independently with the melody, and both can be used to create a two-part piece. Alternatively, all three parts can be sung together.

LULLABYE (GOODNIGHT, MY ANGEL)

Words and music: Billy Joel
arr. Jonathan Wikeley

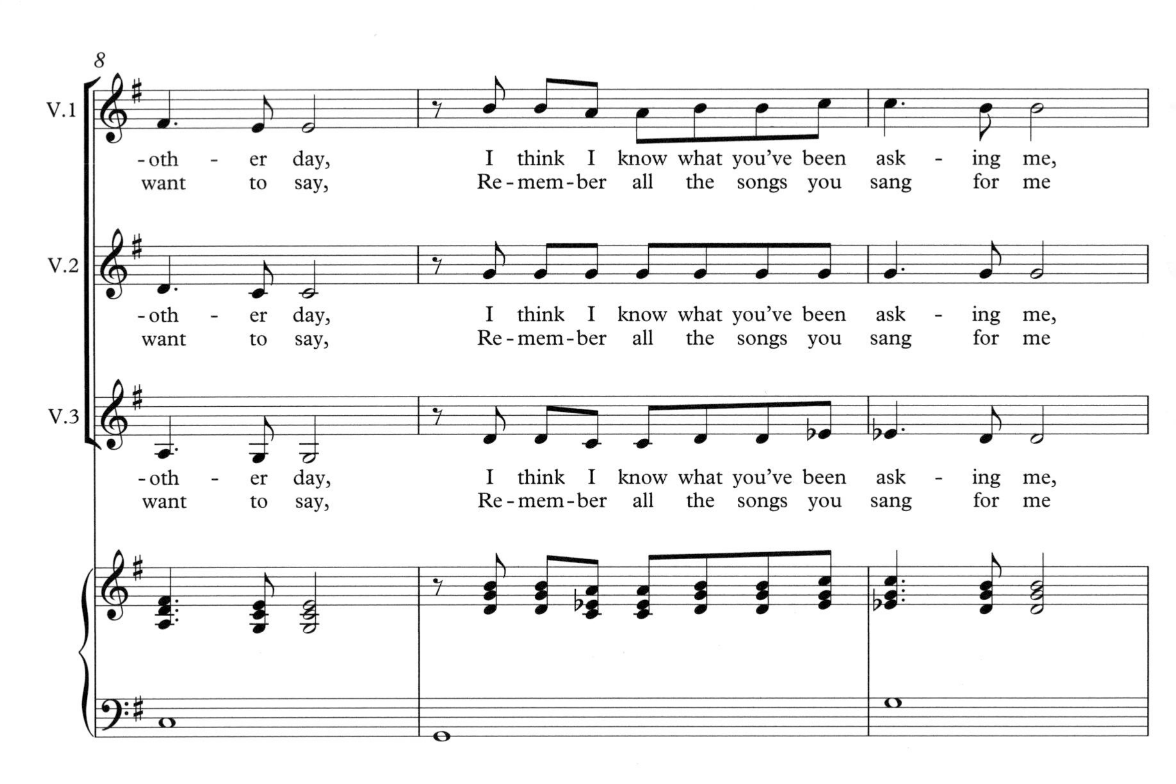
8
V.1
V.2
V.3
-oth - er day, I think I know what you've been ask - ing me,
want to say, Re-mem-ber all the songs you sang for me
-oth - er day, I think I know what you've been ask - ing me,
want to say, Re-mem-ber all the songs you sang for me
-oth - er day, I think I know what you've been ask - ing me,
want to say, Re-mem-ber all the songs you sang for me

11
V.1
V.2
V.3
cresc.
mf
I think you know what I've been trying to say. I prom-ised I would nev - er
when we went sail - ing on an em - 'rald bay; And like a boat out on the
cresc.
mf
I think you know what I've been trying to say. I prom-ised I would nev - er
when we went sail - ing on an em - 'rald bay; And like a boat out on the
cresc.
mf
I think you know what I've been trying to say. I prom-ised I would nev - er
when we went sail - ing on an em - 'rald bay; And like a boat out on the
cresc.
mf

14
mp
leave__ you, and you should al-ways know__ Wher-ev - er you may go,__
o - cean, I'm rock - ing you to sleep,__ The wat-er's dark and deep_
leave you,__ and you should al-ways know__ Wher-ev - er you may go,__
o - cean,__ I'm rock - ing you to sleep,__ The wat-er's dark and deep_
leave you, and you should al-ways know____ Wher-ev - er you may go,__
o - cean, I'm rock - ing you to sleep,____ The wat-er's dark and deep_

18
__ no mat - ter where you are,__ I nev - er will be far a - way.
__ in - side this an - cient heart,__ you'll al - ways be a part of me.
__ no mat - ter where you are,__ I nev - er will be far a - way.
__ in - side this an - cient heart,__ you'll al - ways be a part of me.
__ no mat - ter where you are,__ I nev - er will be far a - way.
__ in - side this an - cient heart,__ you'll al - ways be a part of me.

21
mp

25
VOICE 1
mp
rit.
V.1
doo doo doo doo doo doo doo doo doo doo doo doo doo doo
VOICE 2 (& 3)
mp
V.2
(&3.)
doo doo doo doo doo doo doo doo doo doo doo doo doo doo
rit.

29
a tempo
p
V.1
3. Good-night, my an-gel, now it's time to dream, and dream how won-der-ful your
p
V.2
3. Good-night, my an-gel, now it's time to dream, and dream how won-der-ful your
p
V.3
3. Good-night, my an-gel, now it's time to dream, and dream how won-der-ful your
a tempo
p

32
V.1
life will be, Some-day your child may cry, and if you sing this lul - la - bye,
V.2
life will be, Some-day your child may cry, and if you sing this lul - la - bye,
V.3
life will be, Some-day your child may cry, and if you sing this lul - la - bye,

35
V.1
then in your heart there will al-ways be a part of me.
V.2
then in your heart there will al-ways be a part___ of me.
V.3
then in your heart there will al-ways be a part of me.

38
41
pp
V.1
Some-day we'll all be gone, but lul-la-byes_ go on and on, they nev-er die, that's how
V.2
Some-day we'll all be gone, but lul-la-byes_ go on and on, they nev-er die, that's how
V.3
Some-day we'll all be gone, but lul-la-byes_ go on and on, they nev-er die, that's how
44
rit.
you and_ I will be.
you and I___ will be.
you and I will be.

DON'T LET THE SUN GO DOWN ON ME

'Don't Let The Sun Go Down On Me' reached No. 2 in the US singles chart when it was released in 1974. It can be treated as one long climax, right up to the very last phrase ('is like the sun going down on me'). Elton John keeps the tension building through his inimitable piano technique and careful pacing of the intensity. To give the best performance as a choir, keep some energy in store for the section beginning 'Too late', and again for the section beginning 'Don't let the sun'.

1. There are a lot of words to get used to in this piece. Begin by speaking them in rhythm, so that you begin to get a feel for the different rhythms in each phrase. Divide your choir into two parts, and take it in turns to speak four-bar phrases to each other in rhythm (the other side can clap the pulse). This will both help to familiarise yourself with the words, and encourage listening within your choir.

2. Try matching up the rhythms below with the lyrics they fit with. Which phrases start on the beat (at the same time as the pulse) and which phrases start off the beat?

The melody is in Voice 1, and the piece can be sung in unison or in two parts.

DON'T LET THE SUN GO DOWN ON ME

Words: Bernie Taupin
Music: Elton John, arr. Thomas Lydon

13
V.1
I'm grow-ing tired, and time stands still be - fore me;
V.2
I'm grow-ing tired, and time stands still be - fore me;
16
V.1
Fro-zen here on the lad-der of my life.
V.2
Fro-zen here on the lad-der of my life.
20
mf
V.1
Too late to save my-self from fall - ing,
mf
V.2
Too late to save my-self from fall - ing,
mf

24
V.1
I took a chance and changed your way of
V.2
I took a chance and changed your way of
27
V.1
life. But you mis-read
V.2
life. But you mis-read
30
V.1
my mean-ing when I met you, Closed the door
V.2
my mean-ing when I met you, Closed the door

34
cresc.
and left me blind - ed by the light.
cresc.
and left me blind - ed by the light.
cresc.
37
f
Don't let the sun go down on me; Al-though I search my-self, it's
f
Don't let the sun go down on me; Al-though I search my-self, it's
f
40
some-one else I see. I'd just al-low a frag-ment of your life to wan-der
some-one else I see. I'd just al-low a frag-ment of your life to wan-der

43
V.1
free.
But
los-ing ev - 'ry-thing
is like the
V.2
free.
But
los-ing ev - 'ry-thing
is like the

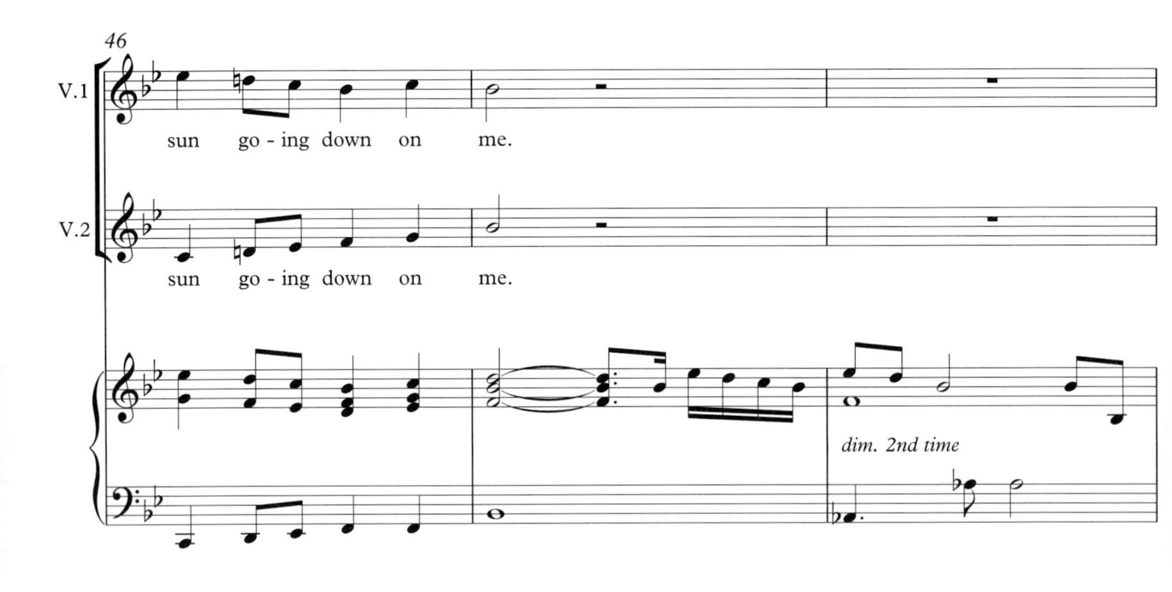
46
V.1
sun
go - ing
down
on
me.
V.2
sun
go - ing
down
on
me.
dim. 2nd time

49
p

IT MUST BE LOVE

'It Must Be Love' was written in 1971 by Labi Siffre, and was most famously covered by Madness on their 1981 album *Complete Madness*.

1 Ask your accompanist (or use the online track) to play the accompaniment up to the start of each phrase in the first verse. In this song, the accompaniment doesn't give you much help in getting the start of the note - and that note varies from phrase to phrase! Practise listening to the accompaniment, and then pausing on the first note of each phrase. Only move off once everyone is singing the same note. Repeat until you are hitting the right notes from the start.

2 A large part of the effectiveness of the first verse stems from the contrast between the strong crotchet pulse against the swung (and frequently off-beat) rhythms in the vocal lines. These lines are much easier to sing than they look on the page. Begin by saying the rhythm of the first 17 bars all together and getting a feel for the rhythm. Note which phrases end on the offbeat and those which end on the beat.

Now divide into two parts. One part claps the four-beat crotchet pulse as steadily as possible; the other part claps (or speaks) the rhythm of the words. Once you've managed this, change the parts over, so everyone has a go at keeping the pulse and saying the words.

The melody is in Voice 1, and the piece can be sung in unison or in two parts. The final repeated section (bars 87-89) can be sung as many times as required.

IT MUST BE LOVE

Words and music: Labi Siffre
arr. Jonathan Wikeley

13
V.1
and I nev-er thought_ I'd feel_ this way,_ the way I feel_ a-bout
V.2
and I nev-er thought_ I'd feel_ this way,_ the way I feel_ a-bout
17
V.1
you.
V.2
you.
21
Straight quavers
V.1
Soon as I wake_ up ev-'ry night, ev-'ry day,
V.2
Soon as I wake_ up ev-'ry night, ev-'ry day,
Straight quavers

25
cresc.
V.1
I know that it's you I need to take the blues a-way.
V.2
I know that it's you I need to take the blues a-way.
cresc.
3
29
f
To Coda
It must be love, love, love, it must be love, love,
It must be love, love, love, it must be love, love,
34
love. Noth-ing more, noth-ing less: love is the best.
love. Noth-ing more, noth-ing less: love is the best.

39
mf
How can it be___ that we___ can say so much___ with-out
mf
How can it be___ that we___ can say so much___ with-out
mf
43
words?
words?
47
Bless you and bless___ me, bless the bees,___ and the
Bless you and bless___ me, bless the bees,___ and the

51
V.1
birds.
V.2
birds.
55
V.1
I've got to be near you ev-'ry night, ev-'ry day,
V.2
I've got to be near you ev-'ry night, ev-'ry day,
59
cresc.
V.1
I could-n't be hap-py an - y oth - er way.
cresc.
V.2
I could-n't be hap-py an - y oth - er way.
cresc.

63
V.1
f
It must be love, love, love, it must be love,
V.2
f
It must be love, love, love, it must be love,
3
f
67
love, love. Noth-ing more, noth-ing less:
love, love. Noth-ing more, noth-ing less:
3
71
love is the best.
mp
oo
love is the best.
mp
oo
mp

77
1.
2.
D.S. al Coda
V.1
V.2
Coda
82
love.
87
f
It must be love, love, love.
3

JINGLE BELLS

'Jingle Bells' was written by James Lord Pierpont and published in 1857. Originally written for Thanksgiving, it soon became associated with Christmas, and has gone on to become one of the most popular Christmas songs ever written.

This piece needs a good amount of energy to it – it wants to sound robust and jolly. Its very nature suggests breathless excitement, but to sing it, you need control over your breathing!

1 Take a relaxed breath in; feel as though you are filling up from your stomach, and keep one hand on each side of your stomach so you can feel what is happening. Now breathe out to a *fffffff* sound, pushing the air up through your body from your diaphragm. Relax, and let the air fill your body again.

Now try pushing the air out quickly, to a *fft fft fft* sound, pushing up all the time from your diaphragm.

Next, go full-on Father Christmas, and do the same exercise to *ho ho ho*, remembering to keep your hands on either side of your stomach so you can feel what is going on as you breathe in and out.

2 Sing the exercise below with plenty of energy, thinking about how you push up the air from your body as you sing. You can sing this to *ho*, *ha* or on any other vowel. Start on any note that feels comfortable.

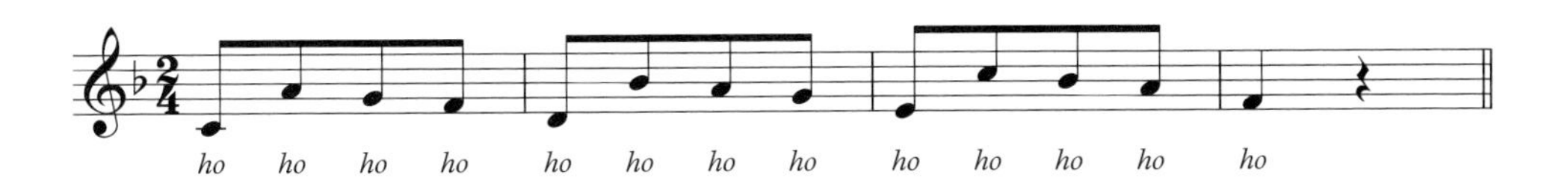

The melody is in Voice 1, and the piece can be sung in unison or in two parts. You may wish to save the canon in the verse section until verse 2. Some jingling sleigh bells won't go amiss in this piece – particularly in the choruses. In the verses, try adding sound effects – '*ho ho ho*' at bar 16 after 'laughing all the way', or 'clip clop' sounds in bar 17 after 'bob-tailed bay'. Don't limit yourself to these – be imaginative!

JINGLE BELLS

Words and music: James Lord Pierpont
arr. Laurence Long

10
one-horse o - pen sleigh.
one-horse o - pen sleigh.
mp
f
13
mp
1. Dash - ing through the snow in a one - horse o - pen sleigh,
2. Now the ground is white, so___ go it while you're young,
mp
Dash - ing through the snow in a one - horse o - pen
Now the ground is white, so___ go it while you're
mp
15
O'er the fields we go, laugh - ing all the way.
Take the girls to - night and sing this sleigh - ing song. Just
sleigh, O'er the fields we go, laugh - ing all the
young, Take the girls to - night, and sing this sleigh - ing

17
V.1
Bells on bob - tails ring mak - ing spi - rits bright, What
get a bob - tailed bay, two - for - ty for his speed,
V.2
way. Bells on bob - tails ring mak - ing spi - rits,
song. Just get a bob - tailed bay, two - for - ty for his,
19
f
fun it is to laugh and sing a sleigh - ing song to - night!
Hitch him to an o - pen sleigh and 'crack' you'll take the lead!
Oh
Fun it is to laugh and sing a sleigh - ing song to - night!
Hitch him to an o - pen sleigh and 'crack' you'll take the lead!
Oh
mf
21
Jin - gle bells, jin - gle bells, jin - gle all the way!
Jin - gle bells, jin - gle bells, jin - gle all the way!

23
Oh what fun it is to ride in a one - horse o - pen sleigh, Oh
Oh what fun it is to ride in a one - horse o - pen sleigh, Oh
25
Jin - gle bells, jin - gle bells, jin - gle all the way!
Jin - gle bells, jin - gle bells, jin - gle all the way!
27
(2° only)
ff
Oh what fun it is to ride in a one - horse o - pen sleigh. Hey!
ff
Oh what fun it is to ride in a one - horse o - pen sleigh. Hey!
8vb

HAVE YOURSELF A MERRY LITTLE CHRISTMAS

'Have Yourself A Merry Little Christmas' was first sung by Judy Garland in the film *Meet Me In St Louis*, released in 1944. The melody covers a reasonably wide range (an octvave and a fourth) which, combined with the mix of scales and arpeggios in the tune, and need for smooth (*legato*) singing, makes this a good piece to practise your technique.

1 Sing the exercise below, which is based on the first bar of the piece. Start on any note that feels comfortable. Stand with your feet placed a little apart, with your head nicely balanced on your shoulders.

Clasp your hands together in front of you, and the phrase ascends, gently press downwards; let your hands rise back up as the phrase descends. This helps you to keep your voice in the same place, which in turn helps you to sing nice, relaxed top notes.

Once you've mastered this, sing the same exercise starting a little higher each time. But keep it relaxed!

2 A smooth tone is needed for this song. To create *legato* phrases, sing any phrase from the piece to a single vowel (*ah* is a good open vowel to start with). Think about keeping the voice in the same place as described above (think down as you sing up) and aim to create a beautiful ribbon of sound.

Now sing the same passage in the same *legato* manner, but this time sing only the vowels of the lyrics. Remember to keep everything joined up. Finally, drop the consonants in, being careful to maintain that continuous ribbon of vowel sounds.

The melody is in Voice 1, and the piece can be sung in unison or in two parts.

HAVE YOURSELF A MERRY LITTLE CHRISTMAS

Words and Music: Hugh Martin & Ralph Blane
arr. Phoebe McFarlane

9
V.1
mf
sight.
Have your - self a
V.2
mf
sight.
Have your - self a
mf
mp
12
V.1
mer - ry lit - tle Christ - mas, Make the Yule - tide gay,
V.2
mer - ry lit - tle Christ - mas, Make the Yule - tide gay,
15
V.1
f
Next year all our trou - bles will be miles a - way.
V.2
f
Next year all our trou - bles will be miles a - way.
mf

18
p wistful
Here we are as in old-en days, Hap-py
p wistful
Here we are in old - en days, The
pp
21
gold-en days of yore, Faith - ful friends who are
gold - en days of yore, Faith - ful friends who are
24
rit.
mf
dear to us Gath-er near to us once more.
mf
dear to us Gath-er near to us once more.
rit.
mf

a tempo
f dolce
V.1
Through the years we all will be to-geth-er, If the fates al-low,
V.2
Through the years we all will be to-geth-er, If the fates al-low,
a tempo
mf
mf
Hang a shin-ing star up-on the high-est bough,
mp
And
mp
And
rit.
Slower
p
have your-self a mer-ry lit-tle Christ-mas now.
8vb

WHITE CHRISTMAS

Irving Berlin's 'White Christmas' was first released as part of the soundtrack for the musical film *Holiday Inn* in 1942. The version sung by Bing Crosby is the world's best-selling single, with estimated sales in excess of 100 million copies worldwide.

1 The phrases in this piece are fairly long and sustained, and a good breath beforehand will be your friend. Look at the first exercise on page 99, take a deep, relaxed breath, and count to 20 at a medium pace, thinking about the rate your breath is leaving your body, so that you come to the end of your breath as you reach 20.

Now, ensuring you stay relaxed, do the same but count to 30, grading the output of air so you come to the end of your breath as you reach 30. You can count further, but the most important element of this exercise is to stay relaxed and think about your breathing.

While you do this exercise you can at the same time do some physical loosening exercises to keep you relaxed. These can include loosely wriggling your fingers, arms or legs (or all three), moving your jaw from side to side as you speak to loosen it, or gently massaging your temples. A conductor or member of the choir can lead this exercise, with everyone else copying them.

2 Of course, the physical exercises described above can also be done on their own. In addition, try the following:

- To loosen the shoulders, bring them up as though you are trying to touch your ears with them as you breathe in. Hold them, and then let them drop, simultaneously letting your breath rush out.
- Group yawning. Yawn together, find the muscle that joins your jaw to your skull and (gently!) massage it to loosen it up.
- Standing well balanced on both feet, stretch both arms out in front of you. Then stretch both arms above your head. Finally, trying to avoid your neighbour, stretch both your arms out to the side. Shake out your arms.

The melody is in Voice 1, and the piece can be sung in unison or in two parts. The harmonies from Voice 2 in the second chorus (from bar 19) fit the first chorus if you wish to sing the whole piece in two parts.

WHITE CHRISTMAS

Words and music: Irving Berlin
arr. Phoebe McFarlane

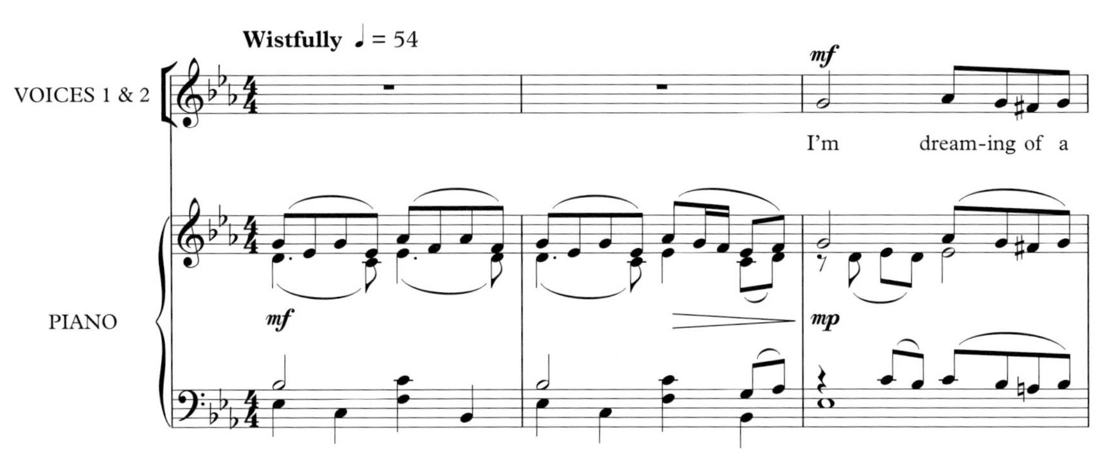

10
poco rit.
a tempo
snow. I'm dream-ing of a white Christ-mas
mf
mp

13
With ev-ery Christ-mas card I write; May your days be mer-ry and
mf

16
mp
bright, And may all your Christ - mas-es be white.
p

19
VOICE 1
f legato
V.1
I'm dream-ing of a white Christ-mas, Just like the ones I used to
VOICE 2
f legato
V.2
I'm dream-ing of a white Christ-mas, Just like the ones I used to
mf
22
know, Where the tree - tops glis-ten and child - ren lis-ten To
know, Where the tree - tops_ glis-ten and child - ren lis-ten To
25
hear sleigh bells in the snow. I'm dream-ing of a
hear sleigh bells in the snow. I'm dream-ing of a
sf
mf

28
white Christ-mas
With ev-ery Christ-mas card I
white Christ-mas
With ev-ery Christ-mas card I
30
rit.
Slower
mp
p
write;
May your days be mer-ry and bright,
And may
write;
May your days be mer-ry and bright,_ and_ bright, And may
33
all your Christ-mas-es be white.
all your Christ-mas-es be white.
like an echo
mf
p
pp

THE VIRGIN MARY HAD A BABY BOY

'The Virgin Mary Had A Baby Boy' is a West Indian carol, first notated from the singing of James Bryce in 1942 when he was 92 years old.

1 Sing the exercise below, putting in as vulgar a slide as you can between each note. As you slide up, clasp your hands together and push them down towards the floor – this helps keep your voice in the same place and helps to avoid stretching up towards the top notes. The slide is important because it keeps the two notes joined. Take as long as you like over the slide and make sure you sing through the whole phrase smoothly and openly.

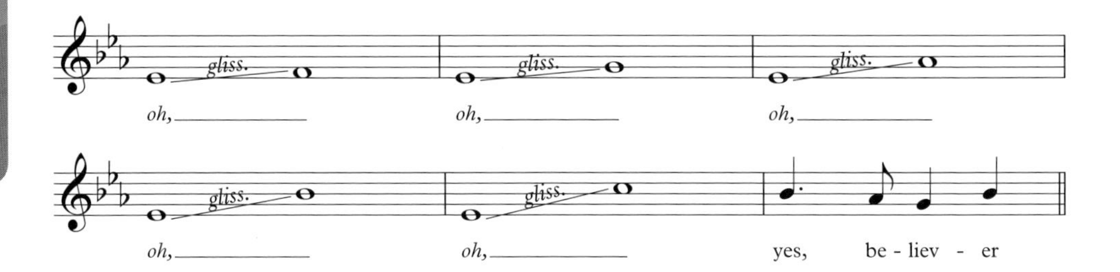

Once you have acheived this (and beware, the temptation to avoid the slide can be great), you can speed up the exercise until you can barely hear the slide. Try not to speed up too quickly – you want to keep the two notes joined together as much as you can.

2 This piece has a very relaxed vibe. Some pieces feel as though they draw you forward as you sing, but this carol should definitely feel more laid back. Stand balanced on both feet; take in a deep, relaxed breath; listen to your fellow singers as you sing.

Now sing the verse with your knees bent – don't worry too much about how you look; only your conductor will notice. As well as helping you to stay relaxed, bending your knees as you sing like this can also take your mind off other technical matters. Obviously, you need to think about what you sing. However, sometimes it's best to clear the mind, open the voice and just go for it – let the details look after themselves.

To sing this piece in unison, start by singing Voice 1 and then moving down to Voice 2 in the chorus (bar 13 and bar 41). The whole piece can be sung in two parts. The optional third part will work in addition to the lower parts, and can also be sung with just the melody.

A bit of gentle percussion wouldn't go amiss in this piece – an egg shaker or similar will give it a bit of style. Do make sure you let whoever plays it have a practice beforehand with the choir, as the rhythms need to feel perfectly secure.

THE VIRGIN MARY HAD A BABY BOY

Traditional
arr. Jonathan Wikeley

10
V.1
ba - by boy, And they say that his name is Je - sus.
ba - by was born, And they say that his name is Je - sus.
V.2
ba - by boy, And they say that his name is Je - sus.
ba - by was born, And they say that his name is Je - sus.
13
V.1
He come from the glo - ry, He come from the
melody
V.2
He come from the glo - ry, He come from the
16
V.1
glo - ri - ous king - dom, He come from the glo - ry,
V.2
glo - ri - ous king - dom, He come from the glo - ry,

19
mf
He come_ from the glo - ri - ous king - dom, Oh___
22
mp
yes, be-liev - er, Oh___ yes, be-liev - er, He come_ from the
26
glo - ry,___ He come_ from the glo - ri - ous king - dom.

29
mf – f
32
VOICE 1
melody
mf – f
V.1
3. The shep - herds came where the
4. The wise men saw when the
VOICE 2
mf – f
V.2
3. The shep - herds came where the
4. The wise men saw when the
VOICE 3 (optional)
mf – f
V.3
3. The shep - herds came where the
4. The wise men saw when the
34
V.1
ba - by was born, The shep - herds came where the
ba - by was born, The wise men saw when the
V.2
ba - by was born, The shep - herds came where the
ba - by was born, The wise men saw when the
V.3
ba - by was born, The shep - herds came where the
ba - by was born, The wise men saw when the

36
V.1
ba - by was born, The shep - herds came where the
ba - by was born, The wise men saw when the
V.2
ba - by was born, The shep - herds came where the
ba - by was born, The wise men saw when the
V.3
ba - by was born, The shep - herds came where the
ba - by was born, The wise men saw when the

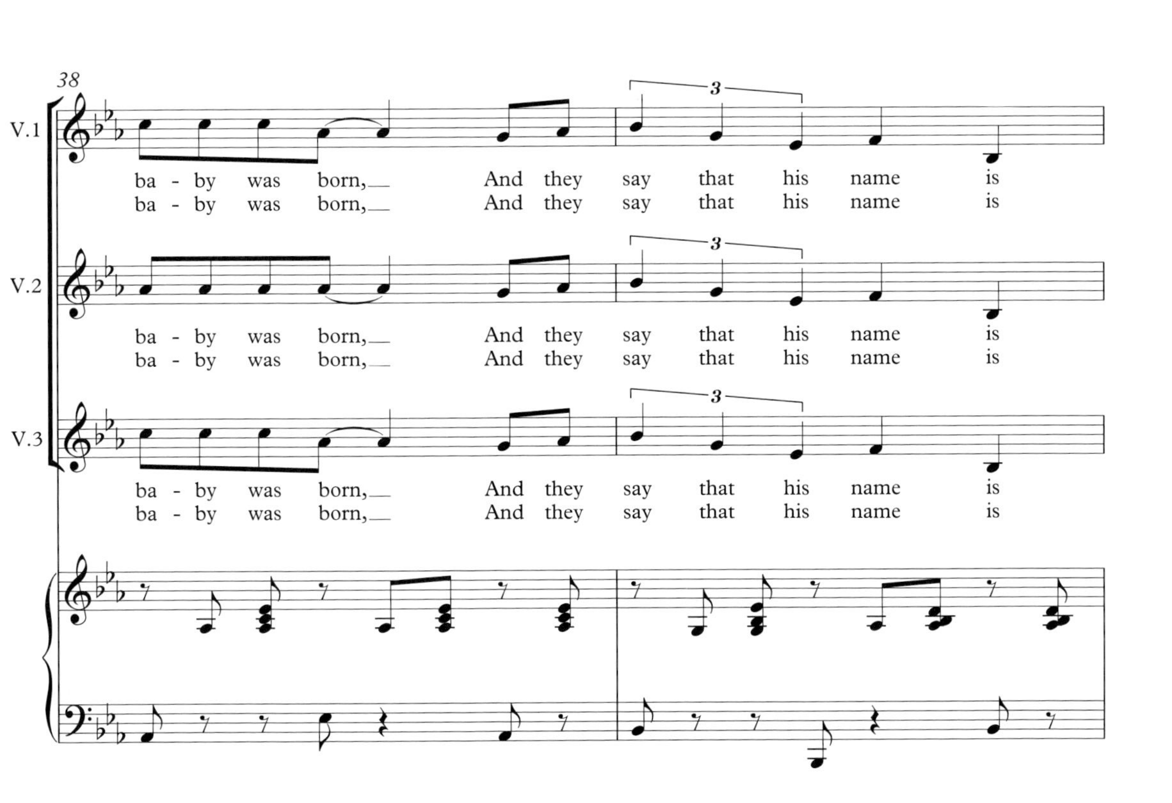
38
V.1
ba - by was born, And they say that his name is
ba - by was born, And they say that his name is
V.2
ba - by was born, And they say that his name is
ba - by was born, And they say that his name is
V.3
ba - by was born, And they say that his name is
ba - by was born, And they say that his name is

40
V.1
Je - sus.
Je - sus.
He come from the glo - ry,
V.2
melody
Je - sus.
Je - sus.
He come from the glo - ry,
V.3
Je - sus.
Je - sus.
He come from the glo - ry,

43
V.1
He come from the glo - ri - ous king - dom, He come from the
V.2
He come from the glo - ri - ous king - dom, He come from the
V.3
He come from the glo - ri - ous king - dom, He come from the

46
V.1
glo - ry,
He come from the
glo - ri - ous king - dom.
V.2
glo - ry,
He come from the
glo - ri - ous king - dom.
V.3
glo - ry,
He come from the
glo - ri - ous king - dom.

49
f - ff
V.1
Oh
yes, be - liev - er,
Oh
V.2
Oh
yes, be - liev - er,
Oh
V.3
Oh
yes, be - liev - er,
Oh

52
V.1
V.2
V.3
mf – f
yes, be-liev - er, He come_ from the glo - ry,__

55
V.1
V.2
V.3
ff
He come_ from the glo-ri-ous king-dom. Oh yeah!

WINTER WONDERLAND

This Christmas favourite is often sung to the accompaniment of sleigh bells on the crotchet beat – a job that can be entrusted to almost anyone without fear.

1 Sing the exercise below, and think about keeping your voice in the same place as you sing. Clasp your hands in front of you as you sing, push down as you sing higher, and let your hands rise up again as you sing lower. At the same time, imagine that you are looking down upon the whole phrase of music – even the high notes – so you can land lightly on them from above rather than stretching up to them from below. Start a little more slowly than you might sing the passage in the piece and build up speed, being careful to stay accurate.

You can extend this exercise by adding in dynamics – sing the lower notes louder than the higher notes.

2 Practise the verse section (from 'Over the ground' to 'hopin' together') with crescendos and diminuendos that follow the rise and fall of the phrases. Ask a volunteer from your choir to direct these dynamics by holding an imaginary ball in front of them at the sides, letting the ball expand for a crescendo and compress for a diminuendo.

Now sing the verse again, but ask the leader to put the crescendos and diminuendos in different places, so the rest of the singers need to watch them carefully.

The melody is in Voice 1, and the piece can be sung in unison or in two parts.

WINTER WONDERLAND

Words: Richard Smith
Music: Felix Bernard, arr. Thomas Lydon

11
V.1
weath - er.
Love knows no sea - son,
V.2
weath - er.
Love knows no sea - son,
14
V.1
love knows no clime,
Ro-mance can blos - som
an - y old time,
V.2
love knows no clime,
Ro-mance can blos - som
an - y old time,
17
V.1
Here in the o - pen, we're walk-in' and hop - in' to - geth - er!
V.2
Here in the o - pen, we're walk-in' and hop - in' to - geth - er!

Lightly
p–f
V.1
V.2
Sleigh bells ring, are you list-'nin'? In the lane snow is
glist-'nin', A beau-ti-ful sight, we're hap-py to-night,
Walk-in' in a win-ter won-der-land! Gone a-way is the

30
V.1
blue - bird, Here to stay is a new bird, He
V.2
blue - bird, Here to stay is a new bird, He
33
V.1
sings a love song, as we go a - long, Walk-in' in a win-ter won-der -
V.2
sings a love song, as we go a - long, Walk-in' in a win-ter won-der -
36
V.1
-land! In the mea-dow we can build a snow - man,
V.2
-land! Snow - man,

39
V.1
Then pre - tend that he is Par - son Brown.
V.2
Par - son Brown,
41
V.1
He'll say 'Are you mar - ried?' We'll say, 'No man! But
V.2
'No! But
43
V.1
you can do the job when you're in town!' Lat - er
V.2
you can do the job when you're in town, in town!' Lat - er

45
V.1
V.2
on we'll con - spire As we dream by the
on we'll con - spire As we dream by the
48
fire To face un - a - fraid the plans that we made
fire To face un - a - fraid the plans that we made
51
1.
2.
Walk-in' in a win-ter won-der - land! Sleigh bells - land!
Walk-in' in a win-ter won-der - land! Sleigh bells - land!

Little Voices

Little Voices is a best-selling series for young groups and choirs.

Each themed book contains five songs which make a perfect introduction to part-singing for young voices.

In addition, each book also contains complete vocal and piano recordings plus piano-only accompaniments to each song.

Little Voices: ABBA! **NOV940808R**	Little Voices: Songs from the Movies **NOV165473R**	Little Voices: Gospel **NOV940643R**
Little Voices: Showtunes **NOV940687R**	Little Voices: The Beach Boys **NOV163625R**	Little Voices: Christmas **NOV940709R**

THE NEW NOVELLO BOOK *of* SHORT & EASY ANTHEMS FOR UPPER VOICES

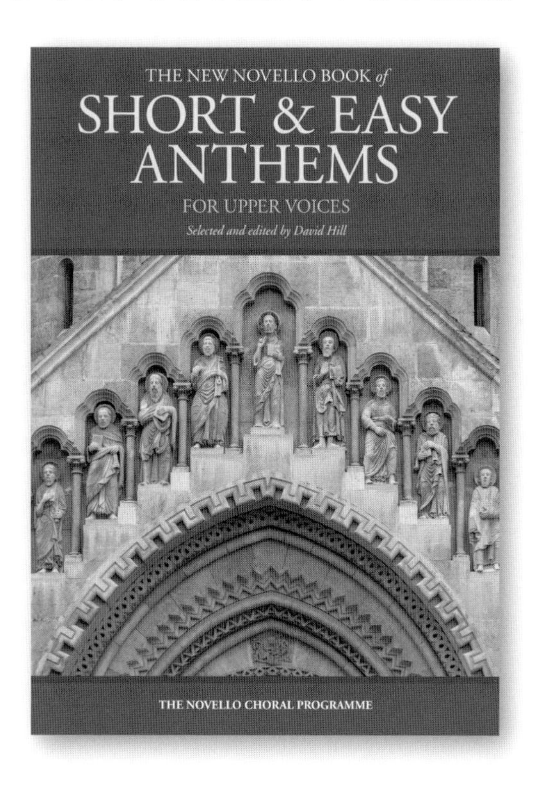

The New Novello Book Of Short & Easy Anthems For Upper Voices is a wonderful collection and an invaluable resource for upper voice choirs who have the desire to sing a variety of beautiful anthems, but who have an limited amount of rehearsal time. Selected and edited by David Hill, this collection includes anthems that are easy to learn and enjoyable to sing but also sound simply fantastic.

With a range of styles, and settings for Eucharist and Evensong, this collection offers a carefully chosen diversity for upper voice choirs large and small. With James Davy's *Sun of my Soul*, Philip Moore's *Listen to the Song of the Children* and Elizabeth Poston's *The Dormouse's Carol*, the selection here is brilliant, including pieces for all occasions and events throughout the year.

NOV295031

This is the indispensable guide to learning how to sight-read choral music. Using special interactive technology, renowned choral educators Ralph Allwood and Timothy Teague take the user from the very basics of sight-reading to a level at which they can sing confidently in a choir.

This guide provides clear explanations, exercises, tips and tricks on:

- basic music theory
- scales and stepwise motion
- larger intervals and awkward leaps
- fast and effective reading of choral scores
- examples from popular choral repertoire
- general good practice for choral singing.

Whether you are 7 or 70, a beginner or an experienced singer, this book will improve your ability to read music and help you to enjoy singing to the full.

This book is supported by SoundWise. It includes a range of interactive digital features:

SoundCheck *powered by* **Match My Sound**

This unique assessment and feedback software lets you use your phone, tablet or computer to help you practise. SoundCheck listens to you sing, then gives you instant feedback on how to improve!

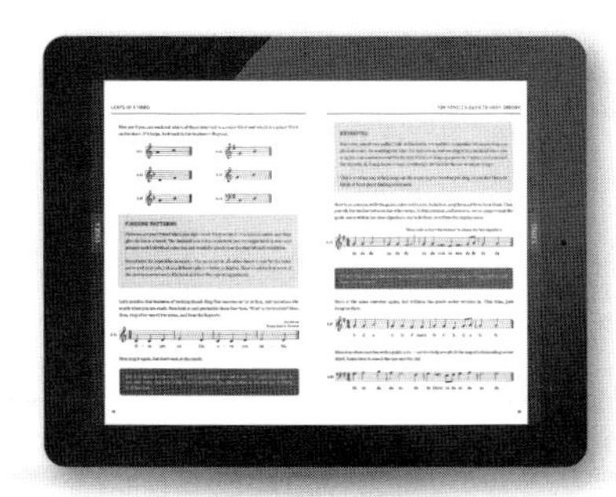

eBook
A digital edition of your book to read on any device.

Video
Tips and demonstrations from the authors.